Jennifer Brown LVI

D0590954

a

THE LINKS OF
THE CANTERBURY TALES

A SERIES OF ENGLISH TEXTS

General Editor: A. J. WYATT, M.A. (Camb. and Lond.)

THE LINKS OF
THE CANTERBURY TALES

AND THE

WIFE OF BATH'S PROLOGUE

EDITED BY

A. J. WYATT

With a Preface by
G. G. COULTON

LONDON
SIDGWICK & JACKSON, LTD.
1936

FIRST ISSUED 1930
SECOND IMPRESSION 1935
THIRD IMPRESSION 1936

PRINTED IN GREAT BRITAIN BY
WILLIAM CLOWES AND SONS, LIMITED, LONDON AND BECCLES

NOTE ON THE SERIES

Two men of distinction have said to me lately: one, "Chaucer is to me a foreign language"; the other, "I have never had the time to study 'Piers Plowman.'" The obstacle in each case was the language: they had not the time, or not the inclination, to solve their difficulties by means of notes and glossaries.

I have heard—and I believe it to be true—that in a hundred readers of Shakespeare there are not more than five who read Chaucer. Yet the Clerk's Tale is easier to read than "King Lear," and far easier to comprehend.

If we regard our poets with awe, reverence, affection, Chaucer stands first among those whom I regard with affection, and largely for that reason it is my ambition to make the five readers of Chaucer into ten. But how? *Modernisation is taboo :* where Dryden and Wordsworth failed the way is barred. Yet, on the other hand, except under the stimulus of examinations, people to-day will not face the discipline of consulting Notes and Glossaries. Then the only hope is to place *all explanations at the foot of the text*. That should appeal, both to the general reader, and to students who wish to obtain a wide, rather than a minute, acquaintance with Chaucer.

And, *without modernisation*, something may be done to normalise the text; all editors of Chaucer normalise. And with good reason: for it is certain that we do not possess Chaucer's autograph manuscript, and that no extant manuscript can claim accurately to represent it.

One editor follows the Ellesmere MS., but he is compelled to abandon its readings at times ; another editor makes his own text from the reading of all the best MSS. : it would be pedantry for any editor to claim that his text is Chaucer's own.

Chaucer's *i* and *y* (vowel) have the same sound-value ; so have his *u* and *w* (vowel). Again, to judge by the manuscripts, he used more than one form for the same word : *e.g.* " noght," " nat," " not." An editor may take advantage of these two facts to simplify his text in a measure, without using a single non-Chaucerian form. Skeat appropriates *y* for the sound of long *i* ; and I have followed his example, but only where the reader was likely to go wrong without that help. Where Chaucer uses two forms for one word, I have used only one—unless the rhyme was thereby marred, and unless a form appeared to be intrinsically important. A usual form is " swich," but the Harleian MS. constantly has " such." And it may be doubted whether the beauty and virtue of " swich " are not equally present in " such " ; it is open to question whether the force and valour of " nat " are not equally present in " not."

With these editorial ideas I approached Messrs. Sidgwick & Jackson ; and they not only encouraged me in my enterprise, but suggested an extension. They said in effect : " What you propose for Chaucer would be equally valid and useful for ' Piers Plowman ' and many other pre-Shakespearean authors and works. Let us have a series." Thus this series originated.

This series of English texts is thus intended, primarily, to introduce to the general reader the masterpieces of our literature before Shakespeare ; it is hoped that it will prove equally useful to the student, as an appetising foretaste of works that are, at a later stage, to be read with more assiduity. For this reason the books in this series are, at least in some instances, both over-annotated and under-annotated ; over-annotated for the general reader, under-annotated for the student ; over-annotated in mere glossing, in respect to which the needs of the general reader greatly vary, under-annotated in the apparatus of scholarship. This appears to me to be justified : the general reader will not be annoyed if there are glosses that he does not need, because he will refer to the foot of the page only when he is in a difficulty ; the embryo student will not expect to find what is not there, because he is for the time a general reader rather than a student.

A. J. WYATT.

The following volumes of the series are now ready :

THE LINKS OF THE CANTERBURY TALES, AND THE WIFE OF BATH'S PROLOGUE : edited by A. J. WYATT, with a Preface by DR. G. G. COULTON

CHAUCER'S PROLOGUE AND NUN'S PRIEST'S TALE : edited by A. J. WYATT

" PIERS PLOWMAN," PROLOGUE AND PASSUS v, vi, vii : edited by C. D. PAMELY

SELECTIONS FROM " LE MORTE D'ARTHUR " : edited by P. L. BABINGTON

THE PROSE MERLIN : edited by L. CRANMER-BYNG

HENRYSON SELECTED FABLES, THE TESTA-MENT OF CRESSID and ROBYN AND MAKYN : edited by H. M. R. MURRAY

PREFACE

I AM honoured by Mr. Wyatt's request that, as a fellow-student of Chaucer, I should say a few words in preface to this volume.

Many of us feel that the best story in *The Canterbury Tales* is what may be called the Story of the Stories; that is, the Prologues and the End-links read as one unbroken whole. It was high time that, after many publications destined to familiarise readers with Chaucer, somebody should present the whole ride to Canterbury in this continuous form; and we may count ourselves fortunate that this is now undertaken by so enthusiastic a student, so able and experienced a teacher, as Mr Wyatt.

Chaucer, like Rousseau, might have said : "You admire the warmth of my writings ; but if only you could read those that I composed on my rambles, yet never wrote ! " What we have from him is only a fragment of what he thought and felt on innumerable rides by packhorse-roads and bridle-ways ; only just so much as he could manage to set in order and write down in the intervals of waiting at Court and sitting at the Customs ; of City society and club society ; of business perambulations ; and of such restless journeys in the royal train as are described by Peter of Blois and other medieval *littérateurs*. But doubtless he had in his own mind a very clear vision of all that road to Canterbury and all those fellow-travellers ; and, if we would seize that vision, our best chance is to do sometimes as Mr. Wyatt enables us to do here, and read the journey straight through without waiting for the stories. From that perusal most readers will rise with a fresh, if only a slightly novel, vision. For, on the one hand, the wealth of what Chaucer has given us, and, on the other, our grievous loss through his interruptions and silences, become more apparent than ever when we approach him from this different angle. But, on the whole, our gain is more striking than our loss ; and that which differentiates Chaucer from all other medieval poets comes out more clearly from this selection than from any other of equal length, except the immortal Prologue.

G. G. COULTON.

ST. JOHN'S COLLEGE, CAMBRIDGE,
    October, 1929.

INTRODUCTION

Groups of Tales

It will be noticed that *The Canterbury Tales* are now always referred to by group and line, the groups being A, B, C, D, E, F, G, H, I. This is a great gain in facility of reference, but the order of the groups is not quite certain. However, the advantage of a generally accepted arrangement is so great that I have followed the A, B, C order without hesitation.

But why groups at all ? Why are the *Tales* not numbered continuously throughout, as they used to be ? The simple fact is that Chaucer, for what reason we can only conjecture, never finally revised his work, left it indeed in a fragmentary state ; it is not even certain that he himself had decided exactly in what order the tales should be told, or on what days they were to fall— for the indications of time are far from clear. The only things free from uncertainty are the route of the pilgrimage, the stopping-places and the number of days : Dartford, Rochester, Ospringe and Canterbury at night, Sittingbourne for a midday meal on the third day, and four days in all. Even if we assume that he did not intend to assign tales to the Yeoman (the *Canon's* Yeoman, who tells one, joined the pilgrims *en route*), the Plough-man, and the five Burgesses, we are still left with an unfinished tale from the Squire, the mere beginning of one from the Cook, and a great many missing links. These missing links are the trouble. When one tale follows another, with nothing between to indicate order or succession, there one group is made to end and the next to begin.   It is my purpose here to provide a menu of Chaucer's feast, with nothing of the gusto of his viands, but serving, I hope, some useful ends : to make a narrative of the pilgrimage, introducing in their places such notes of time and place as he furnishes, and giving the various indications that the links afford as to what tales came next to other tales.

THE PILGRIMAGE

There are two preliminary matters : in what year the pilgrimage took place, and the distribution of the tales over the four days occupied by the journey.

If Chaucer had a particular year in mind, it was most likely that in which he himself made an Easter pilgrimage to Canterbury, in itself inherently a probability.   On this supposition, I consider the year 1385 has most in its favour.   He had lately been permitted to appoint a permanent deputy in what were his most onerous duties, those of Comptroller of the Wool Customs.   In 1385, April 16, when the pilgrims assembled at the Tabard, was a Sunday, and April 20, when they reached Canterbury, a Thursday : no days of the week could be better.

As to the distribution of the tales in the four days, I follow the most commonly accepted arrangement because I have nothing better to suggest.   But it is not satisfactory, for it involves the supposition, as will be seen, that the Knight and the Miller had told two long tales, amounting to 3,000 lines, by 7.30 a.m. on April 17 ; and then we have nothing to fill the long gap of twenty-six and a half hours, until 10 a.m. on the 18th, but the Reeve's Tale of 400 lines and the Cook's fragment of 50 odd.   If the early hours of, say, Monday were so prolific, why were the early hours of Tuesday barren ?   That is the greatest flaw in the present arrangement.

April 17. Group A

At the end of the general Prologue—which might be called the first link, but is not included here because it is in another volume of the series—it is made clear that the Knight is to ' begin the game ' by telling the first tale. At its conclusion (A.3109), every one ' said it was a noble story,' and our Host exclaimed : " This gooth aright," and invited the Monk to tell ' somewhat to quit with the Knight's tale.' But the Miller, who knows himself to be drunk ' by my sound,' rejects the Host's cunning suggestion to ' work thriftily,' and declares that he will ' quit the Knight's tale ' himself or ' else go my way.' The Reeve was a carpenter (Prol. A.614), and the Miller, with an apparently instinctive dislike of him, tells a tale at a carpenter's expense. But first we have from Chaucer a second apology for his coarser tales ; the first will be found in the general Prologue (A.725 *seq.*).

When the Miller's tale was ended, no one seemed to take it amiss except Oswald the Reeve (A.3860), who says : ' This drunken Miller hath told us here, how that beguiled was a carpenter, peradventure in scorn because I am one. And, by your leave, I shall him quit anon.' And the·Reeve's tale follows, at the expense of a miller. But first the Host, in exhorting the Reeve to ' say forth thy tale, and tarry not the time,' has given us the first indication of time and place : ' Lo ! Deptford ! and it is half-way prime [7.30 a.m.] ; lo ! Greenwich ! where many a shrew is in ' (A.3907)—which reminds us that Chaucer about this time lived in Greenwich.

The Prologue of the Cook's Tale has ' while the Reeve spake,' proving that his tale comes next. Then there is the first hiatus : nothing in the Cook's fragment to indicate what follows : nothing in ' The words of the Host to the company ' (B.1 *seq.*) to indicate what precedes.

April 18.   Group B

Of the various topics of interest in the head-link of the Man of Law's Tale (B.1 *seq.*), two alone concern us here. Ll. 1–6 give us the second, and most important, note of time, not indeed the year, but the exact date in the year : April 18 ; and almost as precisely, as may be seen in the Appendix 3 (v), the hour of day : 10 a.m. If no tales had yet been told on that day, we have the explanation of the Host's words : ' Sirs, I warn you, all this company, the fourth part of this day is gone ' ; they may be both a warning and a reproof.

Ll. 33 and 39 give us the teller of the next tale : ' Sir Man of Law, tell us a tale anon ' ; ' Host, I assent.'

The next link (B.1163 *seq.*) shows clearly that the Shipman's Tale comes next. The Host, with a characteristic oath, " for Goddes bones," calls on the parish priest, and brings down on himself a reproof for swearing, which elicits the retort, " I smell a Loller in the wind," and from the Shipman : ' Here he shall not preach ; we all believe in the great God : my joly body shall a tale tell.'

The Host caps the Shipman's tale with (B.1625) : ' Well said ; now long mayst thou sail by the coast, gentle mariner,' and he ' seeks about ' in the company for the next story-teller. His eye falls on ' my lady Prioress,' and his mind is made up at once. ' As courteously as it had been a maid : " Now wol ye vouchesauf, my lady dere ? " " Gladly," quoth she.'

The link at the close of her tale (B.1881 *seq.*) is the only one in stanzas ; it is the best of them all. ' When said was all this miracle,' the Host calls on Chaucer for ' a tale of mirth,' and is offered the only tale he knows, ' a rhyme I learned long ago.' The offer is accepted, and we have the splendid burlesque of Sir Thopas But this proves to be quite outside the limits of

Host's powers of appreciation, and, disastrously for us, though in excellent taste on Chaucer's part, the latter makes the Host interrupt him with (B.2109) : ' No more of this ! Thou makest me so weary of thine ignorance that mine ears ache. This may well be rhyme doggrel.' Chaucer protests at being " stinted," since it is the best rhyme he knows. But the Host is adamant : ' Thou shalt no longer rhyme ; tell something in prose.' Chaucer agrees to give the ' merry tale ' of Melibeus, and begs for no further interruption : ' And let me tell all my tale, I pray.' Oh that our Host had interrupted Melibeus and allowed us to have the whole of Sir Thopas !

" Whan ended was my tale of Melibee " (B.3079), our Host wished that his good wife had heard it, and we have a vivid account of the mutual relations of the pair. ' My lord the Monk, be merry of cheer, for ye shall tell a tale truly. Lo ! Rochester stands here fast by '—so we are nearing the close of the second day, but there is time left for two more tales. Before the Monk tells his, he is mercilessly chaffed by mine Host on his choice of a calling. But he ' took all in patience,' and even offered to tell ' a tale, or two, or three ' ; ' or else first tragedies will I tell of which I have a hundred in my cell.' And he proceeds to tell seventeen of them, beginning with Lucifer.

But after the seventeenth the good Knight can stand no more (B.3957), and he " stints " the Monk as our Host had " stinted " Chaucer. ' Ho ! good sir, no more of this ! I say for me it is a great dis-ease, where men have been in great wealth and ease, to hear of their sudden fall, alas ! And the contrary is joy and great solace, as when a man hath been in poor estate, and climbeth up, and waxeth fortunate, and there abideth in prosperity.' The Host agrees : ' Such talking is not worth a butterfly. But for the clinking of your bells, that on your bridle hang on every side, I should ere this have fallen down for

sleep, although the slough had never been so deep '—
a noteworthy statement as to the condition of the roads.
' Say somewhat of hunting ' (cp. Prol. A.165-92).
The Monk declines, and the Nun's Priest is called on :
' Tell us such thing as may our hearts gladden ; be blithe,
though thou ride upon a jade.' The Nun's Priest is
willing, and he tells the merriest tale of the whole cycle.
Which brings us to the second hiatus, and the end of
Group B.

April 19.   Group C

begins abruptly with the Physician's tale of Appius and
Virginia.   Here give me leave to say, what should perhaps
have been said before, that I have taken full liberty to
appropriate as ' links ' what the manuscripts often call
' prologues.'   For example, I have taken the " Prologue
of the Pardoner's Tale," the close of his tale, and
" Chaucer's Envoy " to the Clerk's Tale, as ' links.'
But in no case have I appropriated any part of a tale.
At the end of his ' Prologue ' the Pardoner says : ' Now
hold your peace, my tale I will begin.' Again, twenty
lines and more after the proper close of his tale, he says :
' But, sirs, one word forgot I in my tale ' ; and that
' one word ' I have included, for it leads to an amusing
scene with the Host.   Moreover, there are prologues
and prologues.   For instance, before the tales of the
Man of Law and the Second Nun, there are prologues
(B.99 seq., G.1 seq.) which are in no sense ' links,' but
are introductions to their tales.

After the tale of the Doctor of Physic, mine Host
says (C.287 seq.) : ' This was a false churl (Claudius)
and a false justice (Appius) ; my heart is lost for pity of
this maid (Virginia).   Thou, Pardoner, tell us some
mirth right anon.'   The Pardoner is willing, but must

---

* There is no note of time in this Group ; hence it is possible
that it ought to come where it is found in some good manuscripts,
between F and G.

first have a drink ' here at this alestake.' Having ' drunk
a draught of corny ale,' he gives us (C.329 *seq.*), not at
first the promised tale, but the most barefaced possible
account of the ways in which, in church, he induces
people to part with their money to him. One example
will suffice : ' If anybody be in this church now who
hath done horrible sin, such folk shall have no power and
no grace to offer money to my relics in this place.' The
result can be foreseen.

At the close of his tale (C.919 *seq.*) he adds : ' Now
is the time to make your offerings to my relics : I counsel
that our Host here shall begin, because he is most
enveloped in sin.' As may be imagined, this leads to a
scene such that the Knight intervenes : ' And ye, sir
Host, that be to me so dear, I pray you that ye kiss the
Pardoner.' Anon they kissed, and rode on their way.
Here is the third hiatus.

Group D

begins with the famous Preamble of the Wife of Bath
(D.1–828). It is as unabashed a document as the
Pardoner's Prologue, and deals with the relations between
the Wife and her five husbands. It is a masterpiece in
two respects : as a revelation of the mind of a coarse
woman of the world in Chaucer's day ; and as a marvellous
example of homogeneity imposed upon the most hetero-
geneous materials. In the latter regard, it bears com-
parison with *The Ancient Mariner*, whose materials can
hardly be drawn from more varied sources ; Chaucer's
sources range from the Bible and St. Jerome to the
Roman de la Rose, and yet everything bears the imprint
of the Wife's personality.

The last line is : ' Now will I say my tale if ye will
hear.' The Friar laughed (D.829) : ' This is a long
preamble of a tale,' and thus gave an opening for the
third quarrel of the journey, with his instinctive foe, the

Summoner. They promise tales at each other's expense, the Summoner's ' ere I come to Sittingbourne,' where was to be the third day's midday meal.

At the end of the Wife's Tale, the Friar (D.1265) indirectly attacks the Summoner, and brings upon himself a rebuke from the Host : ' Ah ! Sir, ye should be courteous ; tell your tale, and let the Summoner be.' The tales of the Friar and the Summoner follow ; the last words of the latter are : ' My tale is done ; we are almost at town ' (D.2294). Here is the fourth hiatus.

Group E

The Host asks ' Sir Clerk of Oxenford ' (E.1 *seq.*) for a merry tale, as usual, and adds : ' Preach not ; tell us some merry thing of adventures.' The clerk complies with the tale of Grisildis, which he learnt from Petrarch at Padua. Chaucer adds to it an ironical Envoy (E.1177 *seq.*), exhorting women to ' let no clerk have cause to write of you a story of such wonder as of Grisildis patient and kind, lest Chichevache,' who fed on patient wives, ' swallow you.'

The next link (E.1213) must come here, because the Merchant opens it with the closing words of the Envoy, ' weeping and wailing,' and he adds : ' There is a long and large difference betwixt Grisildis' great patience, and of my wife, only these two months wedded, the passing cruelty.' The Host naturally calls on him, ' since ye know so much of that art.' He complies gladly, ' but of mine own sore I may tell no more.'

It may have been noticed that there are no notes of time and place in this group, a fact which might leave its place in the series uncertain, were it not that we have three references to the Wife of Bath : one clear reference to her Preamble in E.1685-6, another mentioning her by name in E.1170, and another almost certain allusion in the closing link (E.2437), which also mentions ' this

Merchant's tale' just told. It is, then, a reasonable conclusion that E follows D.

April 20. Group F

opens with the shortest link (F.1–8) : ' Squire, come nearer, and say somewhat of love,' and he obeys. The Squire's Tale, which is " left half told " or much less than half, has an important note of time : " I wol not tarien you, for it is prime," 9 a.m. (F.73). At its abrupt close (F.673) the Franklin heartily congratulates the Squire and disparages his own son in strong terms. But the Host, intent on the story-telling, intervenes with little ceremony, and the Franklin will gladly obey. There is no link between the Franklin's Tale and, in

Group G,

that of the Second Nun. But at the close of the latter we have the longest of the links proper. ' When ended was the life of Saint Cecilia, ere we had ridden fully five miles [from Ospringe], at Boughton under Blean Forest ' (G.554) the pilgrims were overtaken by a Canon and his Yeoman. The former says he had pricked hard ' to ride in this merry company.' His yeoman adds : ' Sirs, now in the morning tide out of your hostelry I saw you ride ' (G.598). Since he is communicative, the Host plies him with questions about his master, who was an alchemist, and about himself : ' Why art thou so dis-coloured of thy face ? ' The Yeoman, nothing loath, talked with so little reserve that the Canon drew near, overheard, and rebuked him : ' Hold thou thy peace ; thou slanderest me here in this company, and eke dis-coverest what thou shouldest hide.' But the Host abets him : ' Tell on, whatsoever betide ; of all his threatening reck not a mite,' And the Canon ' fled away for very sorrow and shame.' The full revelations of the Yeoman constitute his tale (G.720 *seq.*).

GROUP H

'Wit ye not where there stands a little town, which is called Bob-up-and-down, under Blean Forest in Canterbury way?' (H.1). Here our Host says: 'Dun is in the mire,' and, looking round for the next teller, unfortunately catches sight of the Cook: 'What ails thee to sleep in the morning?' (H.16). The Cook is so drunk that, in fury at the Manciple's chaff, he falls off his horse. A farcical scene follows, and then the Manciple tells the next tale (H.105).

GROUP I

begins: 'When the Manciple had his tale all ended,' 'four of the clock it was then, as I guess' (I.1, 5). The first of these two lines makes me regret that *I* is made a separate group; I think it ought to be a part of *H*. We have already seen that the notes of time are unsatisfactory and inconclusive, and the discrepancy between " by the morwe " (H.16) and " four of the clokke " (I.5) is only one more example.

'As we were entering at a thorp's end,' our Host says: 'Now lacketh us no tales more than one' (I.16), and he calls on the Parson for that. 'Thou gettest no fable told for me,' he responds. But the company are sobering down for Canterbury, and " our Host hadde the wordes for us alle " : 'Sir priest, say what you list, and we will gladly hear ; be fruitful, and that in little space.' But in this the Parson is not obedient, for he gives them so long a homily in prose on the Seven Deadly Sins (I.75) that they must have been right glad to reach Canterbury.

THE LINKS

(*Here is the Knight's Tale.*)

THE KNIGHT-MILLER LINK

Whan that the Knight had thus his tale ytold,
In al the route ne was ther yong ne old   3110
That he ne seide it was a noble storie,
And worthy for to drawen to memórie,
And namëly the gentils everichoon.

    Our Hostë lough and swoor : " So moot I goon,
This gooth aright ; unbokeled is the male ;   3115
Let see now who shal telle another tale ;
For trewëly the game is wel bigonne.
Now telleth ye, sir Monk, if that ye conne,
Somwhat to quitë with the Knightës tale."

    The Miller, that fordronken was al pale,   3120
So that unnethe upon his hors he sat,
He nolde avalen neither hood ne hat,
Ne abidë no man for his curteisye,

N.B.—*The first word only of a translated passage is given where no confusion can result ; in such cases the translation is in inverted commas.*

3110 *route* company.
3111 *That he* 'who did not say.'
3112 *for to drawen* 'to be remembered.'
3113 *namely* 'especially the gentlefolk.'
3114 *lough* laughed ; then a strong verb : *so moot I goon*, so may I go, as I hope to retain the power to walk.
3115 *aright* well : *unbokeled*

'the pack is opened,' 'we have made a good start.'
3118 *conne* (optative) can.
3119 *to quite with* suitable to follow.
3120 *fordronken* being very drunk.
3121 *unnethe* with difficulty.
3122 *avalen*, take off, doff.
3123 'Nor had he the courtesy to give place to any man.'

11

But in Pilátës vois he gan to crye,
And swoor by armës and by blood and bones : 3125
" I can a noblë talë for the nones,
With which I wol now quite the Knightës tale."

Our Hostë saw that he was dronke of ale,
And seide : " Abyd, Robin, my levë brother,
Som bettre man shal telle us first another ; 3130
Abyd and let us werken thriftily."

" By Goddes soul," quod he, " that wol not I,
For I wol speke or ellës go my wey."

Our Host answerde : " Tell on a devel wey.
Thou art a fool, thy wit is overcome." 3135

" Now herkneth," quod the Miller, " alle and some.
But first I make a protestaciöun :
That I am dronke, I knowe it by my soun.
And therfore, if that I misspeke or seye,
Wyte it the ale of Southwerk I you preye ; 3140
For I wol telle a legende and a lyf
Bothe of a carpenter and of his wyf,
How that a clerk hath set the wrightës cappe."

The Reve answerde and seidë : " Stint thy clappe.
Let be thy lewëd, dronken harlotrye : 3145
It is a sinne and eek a greet folýe
To apeiren any man or him defame,

3124 *in Pilates voice* a reference to the Mystery Plays, in which both Pilate (esp. in the York cycle) and Herod were given to rant and bombast.

3125 *armes* sc. *Goddes*, as in D.833 and B.3087.

3126 *nones* nonce, occasion.

3129 *Abyd* wait, be still : *leve* dear.

3131 *thriftily* properly, on sound lines.

3133 *a devel wey* in the devil's name.

3136 *alle and some* one and all.

3138 *soun* the sound of my own voice.

3139 *misspeke or seye* speak or say amiss.

3140 *Wyte it* lay the blame on.

3141 *legende* story.

3143 *clerk* the word then combined the notions of ' scholar' and ' priest ' : *set* ' made a fool of the workman ' (the carpenter).

3144 *stint* ' cease thy chatter.'

3145 *lewed* ' ignorant drunken scurrility.'

3147 *apeiren* injure, depreciate.

And eek to bringen wivës in such fame ;
Thou mayst ynogh of other thingës seyn."

This dronken Miller spak ful sone agein,   3150
And seidë : " Levë brother Osëwold,
Who hath no wyf he is no cokëwold ;
But I sey nat therfore that thou art oon ;
Ther been ful godë wivës many oon,
And ever a thousand gode ageins oon badde ;   3155
That knowest thou wel thyself, but-if thou madde.
Why art thou angry with my talë now ?
I have a wyf, pardee ! as wel as thou ;
Yet nolde I for the oxen in my plough
Taken upon me morë than ynough,   3160
As demen of myself that I were oon ;
I wol belevë wel that I am noon.
An housbond shal not been inquisityf
Of Goddes privëtee, nor of his wyf.
So he may findë Goddës foison there,   3165
Óf the remenant nedeth nat enquere."

What sholde I morë seyn, but this Millére
He nolde his wordës for no man forbere,
But tolde his cherlës tale in his manére ;
Me thinketh that I shal reherce it here.   3170
And therfore every gentil wight I preye,
For Goddes love, demeth not that I seye
Of evil entent, but that I moot reherce
Hir talës allë, be they bettre or werse,
Or ellës falsen som of my matére.   3175

3148 *fame* ill fame.
3151 *Osewold* Oswald, the Reeve's name.
3156 *but-if* ' unless thou art mad.'
3158 *pardee* par Dieu, in truth.
3160-1 ' Load myself with needless suspicion, in deeming myself to be a cuckold.'

3164 *privetee* secret counsel.
3165 *Goddes foison* " God's plenty."
3169 *cherles* churl's, boorish.
3170 *Me thinketh* ' it seems to me that I shall,' ' I am inclined to.'
3172 *demeth* deem, judge.
3173 *moot* must (here), may.
3174 *Hir* their (here), her.

And therfore whoso list it not yhere
Turne over the leef and chese another tale ;
For he shal finde ynowë, grete and smale,
Of storial thing that toucheth gentillesse,
And eek moralitee and holinesse :   3180
Blameth not me if that ye chese amis.
The Miller is a cherl, ye know wel this ;
So was the Reve (and othere many mo) ;
And harlotry they tolden bothë two.
Aviseth you, and put me out of blame.   3185
And eek men shal nat make ernest of game.

(*Here is the Miller's Tale.*)

The Miller-Reeve Link

Whan folk had laughen at this nicë cas   3855
Of Absolon and hendë Nicholas,
Diversë folk diversëly they seide ;
But for the morë part they lough and pleyde ;
Ne at this tale I saw no man him greve,
But it were only Osëwold, the Reve ;   3860
Bycause he was of carpenteres craft,
A lytel ire is in his herte ylaft ;
He gan to grucche and blamëd it a lyte :
" So theek," quod he, " ful wel coude I thee quite

3176 *whoso* ' if anyone wishes not to hear it ' ; *list* is usually an impersonal verb with the dative.

3177 *chese* choose.

3178 *ynowe* enough ; pl. form.

3179 *storial thing* matter pertaining to story or history.

3185 *Aviseth you* bethink yourselves, make up your mind; cp. Fr. *s'aviser.*

3186 *And eek men* and also one ; *men*, followed by a verb in the singular, always means the pronoun ' one.'

3855 *nice* foolish, ludicrous.

3856 *hende* courteous, civil, polite, gracious.

3858 *pleyde* were amused.

3862 *ylaft* left.

3863 *grucche* grumble, murmur.

3864 *So theek=so thee ik*, so thrive I, as I hope to thrive ; cp. *theech*, C.947.

With blering of a proud millérës yë,   3865
If that me listë speke of ribaudye.
But ik am old, me list not pley for age ;
Gras-time is doon, my fodder is now foráge ;
This whitë top writeth min oldë yeres ;
Min hert is also mouled as min heres,   3870
But-if I fare as dooth an openers :
That ilkë fruit is ever lenger the wers
Til it be roten in mullok or in stree ;
We oldë men, I drede, so farë we,
Til we be roten can we not be ripe ;   3875
We hoppen ay, whil that the world wol pipe :
For in our wil ther stiketh ever a nail,
To have an hoor heed and a grenë tail,
As hath a leek ; for, though our might be goon,
Our wil desireth folie ever in oon ;   3880
For whan we may not doon, than wol we speke ;
Yet in our asshen olde is fyr yreke.
Four gledes han we whiche I shal devise :
Avaunting, lying, anger, coveitise ;
Thise fourë sparkles longen unto elde.   3885
Our oldë lemës mowe wel been unwelde,

3865 *blering* blearing, dimming ; ' with a story of the hoodwinking of a proud miller.'

3866 *ribaudye* ribaldry.

3867 *for age* by reason of age.

3868 ' My grazing time is over, I now feed on what the stables supply.'

3869 *writeth* makes clear, proclaims.

3870 *also mouled* as mouldy, as old.

3871 *openers* medlar.

3872-3 ' That same fruit continually goes more rotten when laid up in a heap of refuse or in straw.'

3876 *hoppen ay* dance always; cp. Matt. xi. 17.

3877 *a nail* ' a hindrance, the incompatibility of having a hoary head, etc.'

3880 *ever in oon* ever in the same way.

3881 *may* can.

3882 ' Still in our old ashes is fire raked together.' Cp. Gray's *Elegy*, l. 92 : " Ev'n in our ashes live their wonted fires."

3883 *gledes* gleeds, glowing coals : *devise* tell, relate, mention.

3884 *Avaunting* boasting : *coveitise* covetousness.

3885 *longen* ' belong to old age.'

3886 *lemes* ' limbs may well be difficult to control.'

But wil ne shal not faillen, that is sooth ;
And yet I have alwey a coltës tooth,
As many a yeer as it is passëd henne
Sin that my tappe of lyf bigan to renne ; 3890
For sikerly, whan I was bore, anoon
Deeth drough the tappe of lyf and leet it goon ;
And ever sith hath so the tappe yronne
Til that almost al empty is the tonne.
The streem of lyf now droppeth on the chimbe ; 3895
The sely tongë may wel ringe and chimbe
Of wrecchedness that passëd is ful yore ;
With oldë folk, save dotage, is no more."

    Whan that our Host hadde herd this sermoning,
He gan to speke as lordly as a king ; 3900
He seidë : " What amounteth al this wit ?
What ! shul we speke al day of holy writ ?
The devel made a Revë for to preche,
Or, of a souter, a shipman or a leche.
Sey forth thy tale, and tarie not the time ; 3905
Lo ! Depëford ! and it is halfwey prime ;
Lo ! Grenëwich ! ther many a shrewe is inne :
It were al time thy talë to biginne."

    " Now, sirës," quod this Osëwold, the Reve,
" I pray you allë that ye not you greve, 3910

3889–90 ' In spite of the many years that have passed hence since, etc.'

3891–2 ' For certainly, when I was born, immediately death turned on (lit. drew) the tap of life and let it run.'

3893 *sith* since.

3894 *tonne* tun, cask.

3895 *chimbe* the rim of a barrel.

3896 *sely* poor, feeble : *chimbe* chime.

3897 *ful yore* long ago.

3902 *shul* pl. of *shal*.

3903–4 ' A cobbler may as well turn sailor or physician as a reeve take to preaching.' " Ex sutore nauclerus," " ex sutore medicus," were proverbial expressions.—Pollard.

3905 *tarie* waste.

3906 *Depeford* Deptford : *halfwey prime* midway between 6 and 9 a.m., i.e. 7.30.

3907 *shrewe* ill-tempered person, rascal ; about this time Chaucer lived in Greenwich.

3908 *al* quite.

Though I answére and somdel sette his houve,
For leveful is with forcë force ofshouve.
This dronkë Miller hath ytold us heer
How that bigilëd was a carpenteer,
Peráventure in scorn, for I am oon.   3915
And, by your leve, I shal him quite anoon ;
Right in his cherlës termës wol I speke.
I pray to God his nekkë motë breke.
He can wel in min yë seen a stalke,
But in his owne he can not seen a balke."   3920

(*Here is the Reeve's Tale.*)

(*Here is the Cook's Tale—fragment.*)

" The Words of the Host to the Company "

(*Thought to mark the beginning of the second day*)

B

Our Hostë saw wel that the brightë sonne
The ark of his artificial day hath ronne
The fourthë part, and half an hour and more ;
And, though he were not depe expert in lore,
He wist it was the eightëtethë day   5
Of April, that is messager to May ;
And saw wel that the shadwe of every tree
Was, as in length, the samë quantitee
That was the body erect that causëd it ;
And therfore by the shadwe he took his wit   10

3911 *somdel* somewhat,
partly : *sette his houve* (hood)
=*sette his cappe* (A.3143), make
a fool of.

3912 'For it is permissible
to shove off (repel) force with
force.'

3915 *for* because.
3918 *mote* may.
3919 *yë* eye.

3920 *balke* beam ; cp. Matt.
vii. 3–5.

1–14 See Appendix, 3 (v).

8 *as.* This (to us) redundant
as is very common in Chaucer;
cp. l. 13.

10 *took his wit* came to the
conclusion.

C

That Phebus, which that shoon so clere and brighte,
Degrees was five and fourty clombe on highte ;
And for that day, as in that latitude,
It was ten of the clokke, he gan conclude ;
And sodeinly he plighte his hors aboute.   15

"Lordings," quod he, " I warn you, al this route,
The fourthë party of this day is goon ;
Now, for the love of God and of Seint John,
Leseth no time, as ferforth as ye may.
Lordings, the timë wasteth night and day,   20
And steleth from us—what prively sleping,
And what thurgh necligence in our waking—
As dooth the streem that turneth never again,
Descending from the montaigne into plain.
Wel can Senec and many a philosóphre   25
Biwailen timë more than gold in cofre ;
For " loss of catel may recovered be,
But loss of timë shendeth us," quod he.
" It wol not come again, withouten drede,
No morë than wol Malkins maidenhede,   30
Whan she hath lost it in hir wantounesse.
Let us not moulen thus in idelnesse.
Sir Man of Law," quod he, " so have ye blis,
Tell us a tale anon, as foreward is ;
Ye been submitted thurgh your free assent   35
To stonden in this cas at my jugement.

---

11 *Phebus* Phœbus, the sun.
12 *clombe* ' (had) climbed on high.'
14 *gan* did.
15 *plighte* plucked, pulled.
16 *Lordings* sirs.
19 *Leseth* ' lose no time, as far as possible.'
21 *what* what with.
25 *Senec* Seneca the philosopher, first century A.D.
27 *catel* chattels, property.

28 *shendeth* disgraces, ruins.
29 *withouten drede* without doubt, that is quite certain.
30 *Malkins*. Hence " the kitchen *malkin* " in " Coriolanus."
32 *moulen* become mouldy ; cp. A.3870.
33 *Man of Law* the " Sergeant of the Lawe " of the Prologue 309.
34 *foreward* agreement.

Acquiteth you and holdeth your biheste ;
Than have ye doon your devoir attë leste."

" Hostë," quod he, " *depardieux* I assente,
To breke foreward is not min entente.   40
Bihest is dette, and I wol holdë fain
Al my bihest ; I can no bettre sayn ;
For such law as man yeveth another wight
He sholde himselven usen it by right ;
Thus wol our text : but natheles certein   45
I can right now no thrifty talë seyn,
But Chaucer, though he can but lewëdly
On metres and on riming craftily,
Hath seid hem in such English as he can
Of oldë time, as knoweth many a man.   50
And if he have not seid hem, levë brother,
In o book, he hath seid hem in another.
For he hath told of lovers up and doun
Mo than Ovidë made of mencioun
In his Epistellës, that been ful olde.   55
What sholde I tellen hem sin they been tolde ?
In youth he made of Ceys and Alcióne ;

---

37 *Acquiteth you* 'acquit
yourself by keeping your
promise' (*biheste*).

38 *devoir* duty : *atte leste* at
(the) least.

39 *depardieux* in God's name.

41 *fain* gladly.

43 *yeveth* gives.

45 *thus* 'This is what our
citation means' : probably ll.
43–4 were a legal maxim or
proverb.

46 *thrifty* profitable.

47–9 'not already told by
Chaucer, though he is but little
skilled in metre and in clever
rhyming.' It is an obvious inference, now accepted, that the
Story of Constance is an early
tale of Chaucer's, revised for the
Canterbury series and for the

Man of Law. This is the only
passage where Chaucer mentions
his surname ; in the " House of
Fame " 729 we have his Christian
name " Geffrey."

50 *Of olde time* years ago.

54 *made* ' made mention of.'

55 *Epistelles* Ovid's " Heroides sive (or) Epistolæ."

56 *What* why.

57. *made* ' wrote in poetry
the story of Ceyx and Alcyone.'
Chaucer found this story in
Ovid's " Metamorphoses " xi.
The poem here referred to is to
be found in his early work,
" The Book of the Duchess "
(c. 1369), ll. 62–220. On the
whole it is probable that it was
originally a separate poem.

B

And sithen hath he spoken of everichóne,
Thise noble wives and thise lovers eke.
Whoso that wol his largë volume seke,   60
Clepëd the Seintës Legend of Cupide,
Ther may he seen the largë woundës wide
Of Lucresse and of Babilan Tisbée ;
The swerd of Dido for the false Enée ;
The tree of Phillis for hir Demophón ;   65
The pleint of Dianire and of Hermión,
Of Adriáne and of Isiphilée ;
The barren ilë stonding in the see ;
The dreyntë Léander for his Erró ;
The terës of Eleyne, and eek the wo   70
Of Brixseyde, and of thee, Ladómeä ;

---

61   *Cleped* ' called the Legend of Cupid's Saints,' i.e. " The Legend of Good Women."

62   *Ther may be seen.* It is not easy to account for the discrepancies between the actual contents of " The Legend of Good Women " and this *subsequent* account of its contents. Chaucer had written the legends of ten women : Cleopatra, Thisbe, Dido, Hypsipyle, Medea, Lucretia, Ariadne, Philomela, Phyllis, Hypermnestra, of whom Cleopatra and Philomela are not mentioned here ; and eight others are mentioned whose legends, if he ever wrote them, have not survived : Deianira, Hermione, Hero, Helen, Briseis, Laodameia, Penelope, and Alcestis. These eight he may still have intended to write, for in the Prologue to " The Legend " (A.471–4) we read :

Thou shalt, whyl that thou livest, *yeer by yere,*
The moste party of thy live spende

In making of a glorious Legende Of Gode Wemen.

It is more difficult to explain the omission here of Cleopatra and Philomela.   Chaucer may have been relying on his memory ; and he may have been thinking of Ovid's " Heroides," mentioned in l. 55, which include thirteen of the sixteen names here given.

63   *Babilan* Babylonian. For the equivalents of the women's names see the note on l. 62.

64   *The swerd* ' Dido's death by the sword because of the false Æneas.'

65   *tree.* This may be a reference to her death by hanging ; but more probably it alludes to her metamorphosis after death into a tree : *Demophon* Demophoon.

66   *pleint* plaint, lamentation.

68   Skeat pointed out that this refers to the story of Ariadne, and that the island is probably Naxos.

69   *dreynte* drowned.

71   *Brixseyde :* this form is taken from the accus. Briseïda.

The crueltee of thee, queen Médeä,
Thy lytel children hanging by the hals
For thy Jasón, that was in love so fals.
O Ypermistra, Penelopee, Alceste,   75
Your wyfhood he comendeth with the beste.
But certeinly no word ne writeth he
Of thilkë wikke ensample of Canacee,
That loved hir ownë brother sinfully
(Of suchë cursëd stories I sey fy),   80
Or elles of Tyro Appollonius,
How that the cursëd king Antiochus
Bireft his doghter of hir maidenhede,
That is so horríble a talë for to rede,
Whan he hir threw upon the pavëment.   85
And therefore he, of ful avisëment,
Nolde never write in none of his sermouns
Of such unkind abhominaciöuns,
Ne I wol noon reherse, if that I may.
But of my tale how shal I doon this day?   90
Me werë looth be liknëd douteles
To Muses that men clepe Pierides—
' Metamorphoseos ' woot what I mene ;
But natheles, I recchë noght a bene
Though I come after him with hawë bake ;   95

73 *hanging* who didst hang ; this forms no part of her story as told in "The Legend" : *hals* neck.

76 *with the beste* as well as possible.

80 *fy* fie ; ' I condemn.'

81 *Tyro Appollonius* i.e. Apollonius de Tyro, Apollonius of Tyre. The story forms the basis of the play of " Pericles."

86 *avisement* deliberation, determination.

87 *sermouns* writings.

88 *unkind* unnatural.

89 *if* ' if I can avoid doing so.'

91 *Me* ' it would be hateful to me,' ' I should be loath.'

92 *Pierides* the daughters of Pierus, who challenged the Muses to a trial in music, in which they were defeated, and were changed into magpies. ' I am loath to compete with Chaucer, and fail like the Pierides.'

93 *Metamorphoseos* is genitive sing., *liber* (book) being understood ; but it should be genitive plural : *woot* knows.

94 *recche* ' reck, care, not a bean.'

95 *hawe bake* a baked haw, plain fare ; *bake* was still a strong verb in Chaucer, as in Anglo-Saxon.

I speke in prose, and let him rimës make."
   And with that word he with a sobre chere
Bigan his tale, as ye shal after here.

(Here is the Man of Law's Tale of Constance.)

The Man of Law-Shipman Link

Our Host upon his stiropes stood anon,
And seidë : " Good men, herkneth everichon :
This was a thrifty talë for the nones.   1165
Sir Parish Prest," quod he, " for Goddes bones,
Tell us a tale, as was thy foreward yore.
I see wel that ye lernëd men in lore
Can mochë good, by Goddes dignitee."
   The Person him answërdë : " *Bénedicite !*   1170
What eileth the man so sinfully to swere ? "
   Our Host answérde : " O Jankin, be ye there ?
I smell a Loller in the wind," quod he.
" How ! good men," quod our Hostë, " herkneth me :
Abide, for Goddës dignë passiöun,   1175
For we shal han a predicaciöun ;

---

96 *I speke in prose*. This has led to considerable, and sometimes rather silly, discussion. We have already seen (note on 47–9) that the story of Constance is an early verse tale of Chaucer's. He here feigns that the Lawyer tells it on the pilgrimage in prose, as he undoubtedly would have done. But Chaucer knew well enough that his own powers did not lie in prose, and therefore he inserts here his old poem, with some amount of adaptation to the new circumstances.

97 *chere* mien, look, demeanour.

1163 *stiropes* = *sty-ropes*, i.e. climb-ropes, stirrups, originally looped ropes for mounting.

1165 *thrifty* cp. B.46.

1167 *yore* of yore, a while back.

1169 *can* know, knows.

1170 *Benedicite* lit. bless ye [the Lord], the first word of the canticle in "Morning Prayer"; pron. bendiste.

1171 *eileth* ails.

1172 *Jankin* little John, used derisively ; ' O Johnny, so you're there, eh ? ' Priests were often called John, or Sir John (" Richard III." iii. 2, 111).

1173 *Loller* Lollard.

1174 *How* ho !

1175 *digne* worthy, noble.

1176 *han* ' have a sermon.'

This Loller here wil prechen us somwhat."
   " Nay, by my fader soul ! that shal he not,"
Seidë the Shipman ; " here shal he not preche ;
He shal no gospel glosen here ne teche.   1180
We leven alle in the grete God," quod he ;
" He woldë sowen som difficultee,
Or springen cokkel in our clenë corn ;
And therfore, Host, I warnë thee biforn,
My joly body shal a talë telle,   1185
And I shal clinken you so mery a belle
That I shal waken al this companye ;
But it shal not been of philosophye,
Ne of phisyk, ne termes queinte of lawe ;
Ther is but lytel Latin in my mawe."   1190

(*Here is the Shipman's Tale.*)

THE SHIPMAN-PRIORESS LINK

" Wel seid, by *corpus dominus*," quod our Hoost ;   1625
Now longë moot thou sailë by the coost,
Sir gentil maister, gentil marineer.
God yeve this monk a thousand last quad yeer !
Aha ! felaws, beth ware of such a jape.

1178 *fader* the uninflected Anglo-Saxon genitive retained in a consecrated phrase.
1180 *glosen* gloze, gloss, explain, expound.
1181 *leven* believe.
1183 *springen cokkel* scatter tares, " To sowe cockel with the corne " (Gower). Skeat points out that, by a bad pun, Lat. *lolium*, tares, was connected with *Lollard*, and that this accounts for the mention of *cokkel* here.
1185 *body*, self.

1186 *clinken* ' tell you such a merry tale.'
1189 *queinte* quaint, curious, odd.
1190 *mawe* maw, stomach.
1625 *corpus dominus* i.e. *corpus Domini*, the Lord's body : *quod* quoth, said.
1628 *this monk* the hero of the Shipman's Tale : *a thousand* ' a thousand loads of bad years.'
1629 *felaws* comrades, companions : *beth* be, pl. imperative : *jape* trick, jest.

The monk put in the mannës hood an ape,   1630
And in his wivës eek, by Seint Austin !
Draweth no monkës more unto your inn.
   " But now pass over, and let us seke aboute,
Who shal now tellë first of al this route
Another tale " ; and with that word he saide,   1635
As curteisly as it had been a maide :
" My lady Prioressë, by your leve,
So that I wiste I sholdë you not greve,
I woldë demen that ye tellen sholde
A talë next, if so were that ye wolde.   1640
Now wol ye vouchësauf, my lady dere ? "
   " Gladly," quod she, and seide as ye shal here.

(*Here is the Prioress's Tale.*)

THE PRIORESS-" SIR THOPAS " LINK

Whan seid was al this miracle, every man
As sobre was that wonder was to see ;
Til that our Hostë japen tho bigan,

1630 *put* ' made him look like an ape, a fool, and his wife too.'

1631 *Austin* St. Augustine of Hippo.

1632 *inn* dwelling, home ; ' Invite no more monks to your house.'

1636 *as it* ' as if he had been a maid '; his courtesy is shown by the use of " you, ye "; he had just used " thou " to the Shipman.

1637 *leve* leave.

1638 *So that* ' provided that I knew.'

1639 *demen* deem, decide.

1642 *here* hear.

1881 This is the only link in stanzas. Since this link was certainly written for the Canterbury Tales, the fact that it is written in stanzas proves that the preceding Prioress's Tale was also written for the Canterbury series, for on no other supposition can this solitary *stanza*-link be explained. All the other tales in stanzas were early tales inserted later in the series.

this miracle : the little chorister of the Prioress's Tale still sang 'O Alma Redemptoris Mater " after he had been killed by Jews.

1882 *wonder* in Chaucer is noun, adj., and adv. Here it is an adj.

1883 *japen* to jest.

And than at erst he lookëd upon me,
And seidë thus : " What man art thou ? " quod he ; 1885
" Thou lookest as thou woldest finde an hare,
For ever upon the ground I see thee stare.

Approchë neer, and look up merily.
Now war you, sirs, and let this man have place.
He in the waast is shape as wel as I ;   1890
This were a popet in an arm tenbrace
For any womman smal and fair of face.
He semeth elvish by his contenaunce,
For unto no wight doth he daliäunce.

Sey now somwhat, sin other folk han said ;   1895
Tell us a tale of mirth, and that anoon."
" Hostë," quod I, " ne beth not evil apaid,
For other talë certës can I noon,
But of a rime I lernëd longe agoon."
" Ye, that is good," quod he ; " now shal we here   1900
Som deintë thing, me thinketh by his chere."

(Here is Chaucer's Tale of Sir Thopas.)

" Here the Host stinteth Chaucer of his Tale of Thopas."

" No more of this, for Goddës dignitee,"
Quod ourë Hostë, " for thou makest me   2110
So wery of thy verray lewëdnesse

1884   *at erst* for the first time :
me Chaucer.
1885   *What man* what sort of
man.
1889   *war you* make room.
1890   *He in the waast* ' He is
as stout as I am.'
1891   *popet* puppet, doll : *tenbrace* to embrace.
1893   *elvish* elf-like, ab-
stracted, absent.
1894   ' For he enters into
familiar converse with no one.'
1897   *evil apaid* ill-pleased,
dissatisfied.
1898   *certes* certainly.
1900   *Ye* yea.
1901   *deinte* dainty, pleasant.
2111   *lewednesse* blameworthy
ignorance, bad taste.

That, also wisly God my soulë blesse !
Min erës aken of thy drasty speche.
Now such a rym the devel I biteche.
This may wel be rym dogerel," quod he.　　　2115
　　"Why so ?" quod I ; "why wilt thou lettë me
More of my talë than another man,
Sin that it is the bestë rym I can ?"
　　"By God," quod he, "for pleinly, at a word,
Thy drasty riming is not worth a tord.　　　2120
Thou doost nought ellës but despendest time ;
Sir, at o word, thou shalt no lenger rime.
Let see wher thou canst tellen aught in geste,
Or tell in prosë somwhat, at the leste,
In which ther be som mirth or som doctríne."　　　2125
"Gladly," quod I, "by Goddës swetë pine !
I wol you tell a lytel thing in prose
That oghtë liken you, as I suppose,
Or ellës, certes, ye been to daungerous.
It is a moral talë vertuous,　　　2130
Al be it told somtime in sondry wise
Of sondry folk, as I shal you devise.
As thus : ye woot that every evangelist,
That telleth us the peine of Jesu Crist,

2112　*also wisly* ' as certainly as I hope that God will bless my soul.'

2113　*eres aken* ears ache : *drasty* rubbishy, worthless.

2114　*the devel* ' I consign to the devil.'

2116　*lette* hinder.

2121　*despendest* wastest.

2122　*at o* in one.

2123　*tellen* ' tell something in the manner of a metrical romance.' This is exactly what Chaucer had been doing when the Host unpardonably " stinted" him. But " Sir Thopas " was a burlesque, and the Host wanted one of the stock stories of the minstrels. That Chaucer should make the Host interrupt *him* was a masterstroke of good taste.

2124　*leste* least.

2126　*pine* suffering, torment, passion.

2128　*liken* please.

2129　*daungerous* hard to please.

2131　*wise* wise, guise, ways.

2132　*Of* by.

2133　*woot* know.

2134　*peine* pain, grief, torment.

Ne seith not al thing as his felaw dooth ;   2135
But natheles hir sentence is al sooth,
And alle acorden as in hir sentence,
Al be ther in hir telling difference ;
For somme of hem seyn more, and sommë lesse,
Whan they his pitous passiöun expresse   2140
(I mene of Markë, Mathew, Luk and John) ;
But douteles hir sentence is al oon.
Therfore, lordíngës alle, I you biseche,
If that ye thinke I varie as in my speche,
As thus : though that I tellë somwhat more   2145
Of proverbës than ye han herd bifore,
Comprehended in this lytel tretis here,
To enforcë with theffect of my matere ;
And though I not the samë wordës seye
As ye han herd ; yet to you alle I preye,   2150
Blameth me not.   For, as in my sentence,
Ye shal not finden mochë difference
Fró the sentence of this tretis lyte,
After the which this mery tale I write.
And therfore herkneth what that I shal seye,   2155
And let me tellen al my tale, I preye.

(*Here is Chaucer's prose Tale of Melibeus.*)

THE " MELIBEUS "-MONK LINK

Whan ended was my tale of Melibee
And of Prudence and hir benignitee,   3080
Our Hostë seide : " As I am feithful man,

2136   *al sooth* quite true, *or*
all truth ; the same word is both
noun and adj.
2136–7   *sentence* sense, meaning.
2138   *al* although.

2141   *I mene of* I refer to.
2148   *To enforce with* whereby
to enforce.
2153   *tretis lyte* little treatise,
Jean de Meun's " Livre de
Melibee et de dame Prudence."

And by the precious corpus Madrian,
I haddë lever than a barel ale
That godë lief, my wyf, had herd this tale.
For she nis nothing of such paciënce   3085
As was this Melibeus wyf, Prudence.
By Goddës bonës ! whan I bete my knaves,
She bringeth me forth the gretë clobbëd staves,
And crieth : ' Slee the doggës everichoon,
And brek hem, bothë bak and every boon.'   3090
And if that any neighëbor of mine
Wol not in chirchë to my wyf encline,
Or be so hardy to hir to trespace,
Whan she comth home she rampeth in my face,
And crieth : ' Falsë coward, wreek thy wyf.   3095
By corpus bonës ! I wol have thy knyf,
And thou shalt have my distaf and go spinne.'
Fro day to night right thus she wol biginne :
' Allas ! ' she seith, ' that ever I was shape
To wedde a milksop or a coward ape,   3100
That wol be overlad with every wight !
Thou darst not stonden by thy wivës right.'
This is my lyf, but-if that I wol fighte ;

3082 *corpus Madrian* the body of St. Mathurin. His body would not stay in the ground, until it was deposited, according to promise, in France, where it afterwards worked many miracles.

3083 *lever* rather : *barel ale* barrel of ale.

3084 *That gode lief* that dear good creature !

3085 *nis nothing* is not at all ; the double negative, inherited from Anglo-Saxon, is frequent in Chaucer and in Shakespeare.

3087 *knaves* lads, male helpers.

3088 *clobbed* shaped like a club, knobbed.

3089 *Slee* slay : *everichoon* every one.

3092 *encline* bow.

3093 *to hir* ' as to offend her.'

3094 *rampeth* flies.

3095 *wreek* avenge.

3096 *corpus bones* said to be a confusion of two common oaths, " corpus Domini " and " Christes bones " ; but if, with Skeat, we take *corpus* to be meant for a genitive, there is no need to suppose confusion. Cp. l. 3087 and C.1314.

3099 *shape* shaped, created, destined.

3101 ' Who allows himself to be overborne by everyone.'

And out at dore anon I moot me dighte,
Or elles I am but lost, but-if that I   3105
Be, lyk a wildë leoun, foolhardy.
I woot wel she wol do me slee som day
Som neighëbor, and thannë go my way ;
For I am perilous with knyf in honde,
Al be it that I dar not hir withstonde ;   3110
For she is big in armës, by my feith ;
That shal he finde that hir misdooth or seith.
But let us passe awey fro this matere.
    My lord the Monk," quod he, " be mery of chere,
For ye shal telle a talë trewëly.   3115
Ló ! Rouchéstre stant heer fastë by.
Ryd forth, myn ownë lord, brek not our game.
But, by my trouthe, I knowë not your name :
Wher shal I callë you my lord dan John,
Or dan Thomas, or ellës dan Albon ?   3120
Of what hous be ye, by your fader kin ?
I vow to God, thou hast a ful fair skin ;
It is a gentil pasture ther thou goost ;
Thou art not lyk a penant or a goost.
Upon my feith ! thou art som officer,   3125
Som worthy sextein, or som celerer,
For, by my fader soule, as to my doom,
Thou art a maister whan thou art at hoom ;
No pourë cloisterer, ne no novýs,

3104 *me dighte* prepare to go, betake myself.

3107 *do me slee* ' cause me some day to slay a neighbour.'

3112 *that hir* ' who does or says anything amiss to her.'

3116 *Rouchéstre* Rochester.

3117 *Ryd forth* come and take the storyteller's place.

3119 *Wher* whether : *dan* or *daun* master (Lat. dominus) ; cp. Spenser's " dan Chaucer."

3120 *Albon* Alban. The Host had learnt his name, Piers, in the next Link (B.3982).

3123 *gentil* excellent.

3124 *penant* a person doing penance. Cp. General Prologue 205 : " He was not pale as a forpined goost."

3126 *sextein* sacristan : *celerer* the officer in a monastery who had charge of the wine-cellar and provisions.

3127 *as to* ' in my judgment.'

3129 *cloisterer* cloistered monk : *novys* novice.

Bút a governour, wily and wys,   3130
And therwithal of brawnës and of bones
A wel-faring persónë for the nones.
I pray to God, yeve him confusiöun
That first thee broghte unto religiöun.
Thou woldest han ben a tredëfowel aright ;   3135
Haddest thou as greet a leve as thou hast might
To pérform al thy lust in engendrure,
Thou haddest bigeten many a creäture.
Allas ! why werëst thou so wyd a cope ?
God yeve me sorwe ! but, and I were a pope,   3140
Not only thou but every mighty man,
Though he were shorn ful hye upon his pan,
Sholde have a wyf, for al the world is lorn ;
Religiöun hath take up al the corn
Of treding, and we borel men been shrimpes ;   3145
Of feble trees ther comen wrecched impes.
This maketh that our heirës been so sclendre
And feble that they may not wel engendre.
This maketh that our wives wol assaye
Religious folk, for ye may bettre paye   3150
Of Venus payëments than mowë we.
God woot, no lusshëburghes payen ye.
But be not wrooth, my lord, for that I pleye ;
Ful oft in game a sooth I have herd seye."
    This worthy Monk took al in paciënce,   3155
And seide : " I wol doon al my diligence,

3131 *brawnes* muscles.
3132 *A wel-faring persone* a well-favoured, robust person.
3134 *broghte* 'made thee a member of a religious order.'
3136 *a leve* permission.
3138 *bigeten* begotten.
3139 *cope* a priest's cloak, which formed an exact semi-circle when laid out flat.
3140 *but, and* unless, if.
3142 *pan* brain-pan, crown,

in allusion to the tonsure.
3143 *lorn* the old past participle of " lose," which was then a strong verb ; it is still kept in " forlorn."
3145 *borel men* common men, laymen.
3146 *impes* shoots ; offspring.
3148 *may* can.
3152 *lussheburghes* base coins, imported from Luxembourg ; hence the name.

As fer as souneth into honestee,
To tellë you a tale, or two, or three.
And if you list to herkne hiderward,
I wol you seyn the lyf of Seint Edward ;   3160
Or ellës first tragédies wol I telle,
Of which I have an hundred in my celle.
Tragédie is to seyn a certein storie,
As oldë bokës maken us memórie,
Of him that stood in greet prosperitee   3165
And is yfallen out of heigh degree
Into misérie, and endeth wrecchedly.
And they been versifiëd comunly
Of six feet, which men clepe exametron.
In prose eek been endited many oon,   3170
And eek in metre in many a sondry wise.
Lo ! this declaring oughte ynough suffise.
Now herkneth, if you liketh for to here.
But first I you biseche in this matere :
Though I by ordre tellë not thise thinges,   3175
Be it of popës, emperours, or kinges,
After hir agës as men writen finde,
But telle hem som bifore and som bihinde,
As it now comth unto my rémembráunce,
Have me excusëd of myn ignoraunce.   3180

3157 *souneth into* tends to, is compatible with : *honestee* honour, uprightness.

3159 *hiderward* to me.

3160 *Seint Edward* Edward the Confessor (1041–66), the patron saint of England until superseded in the 13th century by St. George.

3162 *celle* a priory subordinate to a great abbey. The Monk was prior of his cell (Prol. 172).

3164 *maken us memorie* remind us, bring to our mind.

3169 *men clepe exametron* men call hexameter. The reference is to Latin works, such as Ovid's "Metamorphoses."

3170 *In prose.* Boccaccio's "De Casibus Virorum Illustrium," which Chaucer used in the Monk's Tale, is in prose.

3171 'And also in various metres (other than the hexameter)' ; *e.g.* the tragedies of Seneca.

3173 *if you liketh* if it pleases you.

3175 *by ordre* in order.

3177 'According to their epochs, as men find them written.'

(Here is the Monk's Tale : a series of gloomy " tragedies "
of the misfortunes of great men.)

THE MONK-NUN'S PRIEST LINK

" Ho ! " quod the Knight, " good sir, no more of this !
That ye han seid is right ynough, ywis,
And muchel more ; for lytel hevinesse
Is right ynough for muchel folk, I gesse.   3960
I seye for me it is a greet disese,
Wheras men han ben in greet welthe and ese,
To heren of hir sodein fal, allas !
And the cóntrarie is joye and greet solas,
As whan a man hath ben in poor estat,   3965
And climbeth up, and wexeth fortunat,
And ther abideth in prosperitee ;
Such thing is gladsom, as it thinketh me,
And of such thing were goodly for to telle."

" Ye," quod our Hostë, " by Seint Poulës belle,   3970
Ye sey right sooth ; this Monk, he clappeth loude ;
He spak how ' Fortune covered with a cloude '
I noot never what, and als of a ' tragédie '
Right now ye herde ; and pardee ! no remédie
It is for to biwaillë ne compleine   3975
That that is doon ; and als it is a peine,
As ye han seid, to here of hevinesse.
Sir Monk, no more of this, so God you blesse !
Your tale anoyeth al this companye ;
Such talking is not worth a boterflye,   3980

3957   *Ho !* Stop ! Hold !
3958   *right   ynough*   quite
enough : *ywis* indeed, certainly.
3960   *muchel* many, most.
3961   *for me* for my part
disese trouble, distress, misery.
3962   *wheras* where, when.
3964   *solas* relief, cheer.

3968   *thinketh me* seems to me.
3969   *goodly* fitting, meet.
3970   *Poules* Paul's.
3971   *clappeth* talks, chatters.
3973   *noot never* never know
(not), have no idea : *als* also.
3977   *ye* you (the Knight).
3979   *anoyeth* displeases.

For therin is ther no disport ne game.
Wherfore, sir Monk, or dan Piers by your name,
I prey you hertely, tell us somwhat elles ;
For sikerly, nere clinking of your belles
That on your bridel hange on every syde,   3985
By heven King, that for us allë dyde,
I sholde er this han fallen doun for slepe,
Although the slough had never ben so depe ;
Than had your talë al ben told in vein :
For certeinly, as that thise clerkës seyn,   3990
' Wheras a man may have noon audience,
Noght helpeth it to tellen his sentence ' ;
And wel I woot the substance is in me,
If any thing shal wel reported be.
Sir, sey somwhat of hunting, I you preye."   3995
    " Nay," quod this Monk, " I have no lust to pleye ;
Now let another telle, as I have told."
    Than spak our Host with rudë speche and bold,
And seide unto the Nonnës Preest anon :
" Com neer, thou preest, com hider, thou Sir John ;   4000
Tell us such thing as may our hertës glade ;
Be blithë, though thou ryde upon a jade.

3981   *disport* amusement, diversion.

3984   *nere* were it not for the. Cp. Prologue A.169–171.

3986   *dyde* died.

3988   *had* ' had been never so deep.'

3992   *Noght* ' it is useless to preach his sermon.' Skeat quotes Ecclesiasticus xxxii. 6 (Vulgate) : " Ubi auditus non est, non effundas sermonem." In the Apocrypha (Revised Version) there is nothing nearer to this than " Pour not out talk where there is a performance of music."

3993–4. In Prologue A.814 the Host was requested to be

" of our tales juge and reportour." He here asserts that he has the necessary qualifications.

3994   *shal* is to, has to.

3995   *hunting :* see the character of the Monk in the General Prologue.

3998   *rude* rough, unmannerly.

4000   *Sir :* the title, *Sir*, was usually given by courtesy to priests, both regular and secular : *thou* is part of the Host's " rudeness " ; compare his *ye* to the Knight.

4001   *glade* gladden.

4002   *jade* poor horse, hack, " rouncy " (Prol. A.390).

B

What though thyn hors be bothë foul and lene ?
If he wol serve thee, rekkë not a bene ;
Look that thyn hert be mery evermo."   4005
    " Yis, sir," quod he, " yis, Host, so moot I go !
But I be mery, ywis I wol be blamed."
    And right anon his tale he hath attamed,
And thus he seide unto us everichon,
This swetë preest, this goodly man, sir John.   4010

         (*Here is the Nun's Priest's Tale.*)

    (*Here is the Doctor's Tale of Appius and Virginia.*)

THE DOCTOR-PARDONER LINK

C

Our Hostë gan to swere as he were wood :
" Harrow ! " quod he, " by nailes and by blood !
This was a fals cherl and a fals justíse.
As shameful deeth as hertë may devise   290
Come to thise jugës and hir advocats !
Algate this sely maide is slain, allas !
Allas ! to derë boughtë she beautee.
Wherfore I seye al day, as men may see,
That yiftës of fortúne and of natúre   295
Been cause of deeth to many a creäture.
Hir beautee was hir deeth, I dar wel sayn ;

4003 *lene* lean, like the
Clerk's (Prol. A.287).
  4004 *rekke* ' reck not a bean,'
' care not a straw.'
  4006 *Yis*, yes, is a stronger
affirmative than *ye*, yea : so
moot see A.3114.
  4008 *attamed* broached, be-
gun ; cp. Fr. *entamer* to make
the first cut in (a cake).

287 *wood* mad.

288 *Harrow !* a cry for help
addressed to a man's lord ; still
used in the Channel Islands
(v. *N.E.D.*) : *nailes* those which
nailed Christ to the cross.
  289 *cherl . . . justise* Claudius
and his master Appius in the
Doctor's Tale.
  292 *Algate* in any case : *sely*
simple, innocent (our word
" silly ").
  293 *to dere* too dear.

Allas ! so pitously as she was slayn !
Of bothë yiftës that I speke of now
Men han ful oftë morë harm than prow.   300
But trewëly, myn ownë maister dere,
This is a pitous talë for to here ;
But nathëles, passe over, is no fors.
I pray to God, so save thy gentil cors,
Thyn ypocras and eek thy galiánes,   306
And every boist ful of thy letuárie ;
God blesse hem, and our lady Seintë Márie.
So moot I theen ! thou art a proprë man,
And lyk a prelat, by Seint Ronyän !   310
Seide I not wel, I can not speke in terme ?
But wel I woot thou doost myn herte to erme,
That I almost have caught a cardiacle.
By corpus bonës ! but I have triacle,
Or elles a draught of moiste and corny ale,   315
Or but I here anon a mery tale,
Myn herte is lost for pitee of this maide.
Thou, bel amy, thou Pardoner," he saide,
" Tell us som mirthe or japës right anon."
    " It shal be doon," quod he, " by Seint Ronyon !   320

---

299 *bothe yiftes* those of fortune and of nature.

300 *prow* gain, advantage.

301 *maister* the Doctor.

303 *passe* ' let us change the
subject ; it is no matter.'

304 *so* redundant : *cors* body.

306 *ypocras* hippocras, a cor-
dial made of wine and spices :
galianes drinks named after
Galen, medicines (Skeat), as
ypocras comes from Hippocrates ;
Drennan boldly suggests that the
Host means " gallons."

307 *boist* box : *letuarie* elec-
tuary, such as brimstone and
treacle.

309 *theen* thrive : *propre*
handsome.

310 *prelat* dignitary of the
Church : *Seint Ronyan = Ronyon*
(320), the St. Ronan of Scott's
novel, " St. Ronan's Well " ;
little is known about him.

311 *in terme* in correct terms,
set phrases.

312 *doost* ' causest my heart
to grieve.'

313 *cardiacle* spasm, pain at
the heart, for which the remedy
was a " confortative," such as ale.

314 *triacle* (" treacle ") a
sovereign remedy ; originally a
remedy for a wound caused by a
wild beast.

315 *moiste* ' new ale tasting
well of malt.'

318 *bel amy* good friend.

C

But first," quod he, " here at this alë-stake
I wol both drinke and eten of a cake."
　　But right anon the gentils gonne to crye :
" Nay, let him telle us of no ribaudye ;
Tell us som moral thing, that we may lere　　　325
Som wit, and thannë wol we gladly here."
　　" I graunte, ywis," quod he, " but I moot thinke
Upon som honest thing whyl that I drinke."

THE PARDONER'S PROLOGUE

" Lordings," quod he, " in chirches whan I preche,
I peinë me to han an hautein speche,　　　　　330
And ring it out as round as gooth a belle,
For I can al by rotë that I telle.
My theme is alwey oon, and ever was :
' Radix malorum est cupiditas.'
First I pronouncë whennës that I come,　　　335
And than my bullës shewe I, alle and some.
Our ligë lordës seel on my patente,
That shewe I first, my body to warente,
That no man be so bold, ne preest ne clerk,
Me to destourbe of Cristës holy werk ;　　　340
And, after that, than telle I forth my tales ;

321　*ale-stake* stood out hori-
zontally from an inn, and bore a
garland (see Prol. A.666) or a
" bush " ; here used for the inn
itself.

322　*of a cake* some bread.

323　*gonne*, pl. of *gan*, began.

324　*ribaudye* ribaldry.

325　*lere* learn, properly
" teach " ; the two words were
often confused.

326　*wit* knowledge, wisdom.

328　*honest* decent.

330　*peine me* take pains :
hautein loud.

333　*oon* one.

334　" Radix enim omnium
malorum est cupiditas," 1 Tim.
vi. 10 (Vulgate) ; " For the love
of money is the root of all evil "
(A.V.).

335　*pronounce whennes that*
declare whence.

337　*Our lige lordes* ' the seal
on the Pope's official permission
to beg for alms.'

338　*warente* protect from
danger.

339　*clerk* priest and scholar,
sometimes scholar only, as here.

340　*of* from, in.

Bullës of popës and of cardinales,
Of patriarkes and bishoppës I shewe ;
And in Latýn I speke a wordës fewe
To saffron with my predicaciöun, 345
And for to stire hem to devociöun.
Than shewe I forth my longë cristal stones,
Ycrammëd ful of cloutës and of bones ;
Relíkes been they, as wenen they echoon.
Than have I in latoun a sholder boon 350
Which that was of an holy Jewës shepe.
   ' Good men,' I seye, ' taak of my wordes kepe :
If that this boon be wasshe in any welle,
If cow or calf or sheep or oxë swelle,
That any worm hath ete, or worm ystonge, 355
Taak water of that welle and wassh his tonge,
And it is hool anon ; and forthermore
Of pokkës and of scabbe and every sore
Shal every sheep be hool, that of this welle
Drinketh a draughte : taak kepe eek what I telle. 360
If that the goodman, that the beestës oweth,
Wol every wyke, er that the cok him croweth,
Fastingë drinken of this welle a draughte,

---

343 *patriarkes* bishops second only to the Pope in episcopal rank, and next above primates.

345 *To saffron* ' to give a spice and a tinge of learning to my sermon.'

347 *cristal stones* reliquaries faced with rock-crystal. Cp. Prologue A.699, 700.

348 *cloutes* rags.

349 *wenen* ween, suppose, expect : *echoon* each one.

350 *latoun* latten, a mixed metal of which brasses were made. Divination by means of a sheep's shoulder bone must have been widely practised, for it is often referred to, and was still in vogue in the Highlands of Scotland down to c. 1800.

351 *holy Jewes* is certainly the holy Jew of l. 364, where the association with beasts multiplying has suggested that Jacob is meant. See Genesis xxx.

352 *kepe* heed.

353 *wasshe* washed, then a strong verb.

355 *ete* eaten ; ' that any snake has bitten or stung.'

357 *hool* whole (which has no right to the *w*).

358 *pokkes* " pox "=pocks, pustules.

361 *goodman* master of the house, farmer : *oweth* owns.

362 *wyke* week.

As thilkë holy Jew our eldres taughte,
His beestës and his stoor shal multiplye.   365
And, sirs, also it heeleth jalousye ;
For, though a man be falle in jalous rage,
Lat maken with this water his potage,
And never shal he more his wyf mistriste,
Though he the sooth of hir defaultë wiste—   370
Al had she taken preestës two or three.
Heer is a miteyn eek that ye may see :
He that his hand wol putte in this miteyn,
He shal have multiplying of his grain,
Whan he hath sowën, be it whete or otes,   375
So that he offre pens or ellës grotes.
    Good men and women, o thing warne I you :
If any wight be in this chirche now,
That hath doon sinnë horrible, that he
Dar not for shame of it yshriven be,   380
Or any womman, be she yong or old,
That hath ymaad hir housbond cokëwold,
Such folk shal have no power ne no grace
To offren to my relikes in this place.
And whoso findeth him out of such blame,   385
He wol come up and offre in Goddës name,
And I assoille him by the auctoritee
Which that by bulle ygraunted was to me.'
    By this gaude have I wonnë, yeer by yeer,
An hundred mark sith I was pardoner.   390

---

364 *eldres* ancestors ; but *our* jus is nottified.

365 *stoor* store cattle, lean cattle fattened later on.

368 *potage* broth.

371 *taken* received as lovers.

372 *miteyn* mitten, glove.

375 *otes* oats.

376 *grotes* groats, fourpenny pieces.

380 *of it* 'confess it,' 'be absolved through confession.'

382 *cokewold* cuckold, the husband of an unfaithful wife.

384 *offren* make a donation as an act of worship.

385 *out of* 'blameless in such matters.'

387 *assoille* absolve, shrive.

389 *gaude* trick.

390 *mark* 13s. 4d. *An hundred mark* then would be about £700 now.

I stondë lyk a clerk in my pulpet,
And whan the lewëd peple is doun yset,
I prechë so as ye han herd bifore,
And telle an hundred falsë japës more.
Than peyne I me to strecchë forth the nekke,   395
And est and west upon the peple I bekke,
As dooth a dowvë sitting on a berne ;
Myn handës and my tongë goon so yerne
That it is joye to see my bisynesse.
Of avarice and of such cursednesse   400
Is al my preching, for to make hem free
To yeve hir pens, and namely unto me ;
For myn entente is not but for to winne,
And nothing for correctiöun of sinne.
I rekkë, never, whan that they been beried,   405
Though that hir soulës goon a blakëberied.
For certës many a predicaciöun
Comth oftëtime of yvel entenciöun ;
Som for plesaunce of folk and flaterye,
To been avauncëd by ypocrisye,   410
And som for veinë glorie, and som for hate :
For, whan I dar noon oother weyes debate,
Than wol I stinge him with my tongë smerte
In preching, so that he shal not asterte
To been defamed falsly, if that he   415
Hath trespased to my brethren or to me.
For, though I tellë noght his propre name,

---

392 *lewed* ignorant : *is doun yset* are seated.

394 *false* untrue, deceptive.

396 *bekke* nod.

397 *dowve* pigeon : *berne* barn.

398 *goon so yerne* move so quickly.

405 *beried* buried.

406 *goon* ' go a blackberry-ing ': in effect, ' I don't care what becomes of their souls.' The ending *-ed*, with its earlier forms *-eth*, *-ath*, marks a verbal noun.

409. *Som for plesaunce of* one to please.

410 *been avaunced* gain one's ends ; cp. Prologue A.246.

412 *weyes* is not pl., but an adverbial genitive ; ' in no other way.'

413 *smerte* sharply.

414 *asterte* ' escape being tra-duced.'

Men shal wel knowë that it is the same
By signës and by othere circumstances.
Thus quite I folk that doon us displesances ;   420
Thus spitte I out my venim under hewe
Of holynesse, to semen holy and trewe.

   But shortly myn entente I wol devise :
I preche of no thing but for coveitise ;
Therfore my theme is yet, and ever was :   425
' Radix malorum est cupiditas.'
Thus can I preche again that samë vice
Which that I use, and that is avarice.
But, though myself be gilty in that sinne,
Yet can I maken oother folk to twinne   430
From avarice, and sorë to repente.
But that is not my principal entente :
I prechë nothing but for coveitise.
Of this matere it oughte ynogh suffise.
Than telle I hem ensamples many oon   435
Of olde stories longë time agoon ;
For lewëd peple loven talës olde ;
Such thingës can they wel reporte and holde.
What ! trowë ye, the whilës I may preche,
And winnë gold and silver for I teche,   440
That I wol live in poverte wilfully ?
Nay, nay, I thoughte it never, trewëly,
For I wol preche and begge in sondry landes ;
I wol not do no labour with myn handes,
Ne makë baskettës and live therby,   445

---

420   *quite* requite, repay.
421   *hewe* hue, colour, pretence.
423   *shortly* briefly.
427   *again* against.
430   *twinne* depart.
432   *that* repentance.
433   *nothing* ' only against covetousness.'
439   *trowe* imagine, believe.

440   *for* because ; ' by teaching.'
441   *wilfully* voluntarily.
445   *baskettes.* In " Piers Plowman " we read that St. Paul made paniers. It is strange if both authors confused tent-making (Acts xviii. 3) with basket-making. Skeat points out that St. Arsenius (*c.* 400 A.D.) is represented as weaving baskets.

Because I wol not beggen idelly.
I wol noon of the apostles countrefete;
I wol have money, wollë, chese, and whete,
Al were it yeven of the pourest page,
Or of the pourest widwe in a villáge,   450
Al sholde hir children stervë for famíne.
Nay, I wol drinkë licour of the vine,
And have a joly wenche in every toun.
But herkneth, lordings, in conclusiöun:
Your liking is that I shal telle a tale.   455
Now have I dronke a draughte of corny ale,
By God! I hope I shal you telle a thing
That shal, by resoun, been at your liking.
For, though myself be a ful vicious man,
A moral tale yet I you tellë can,   460
Which I am wont to prechë, for to winne.
Now hold your pees; my tale I wol beginne."

(*Here is the Pardoner's Tale.*)

THE PARDONER-WIFE OF BATH LINK

" But, sirs, o word forgat I in my tale:
I have relíkes and pardon in my male,   920
As fair as any man in Engëlond,
Which were me yeven by the popës hond.
If any of you wol, of devociöun,
Offren, and han myn absoluciöun,
Com forth anon and kneleth here adoun,   925
And mekëly receiveth my pardóun;

---

447 *countrefete* imitate.
448 *wolle* wool.
451 *sterve* die.
454 *herkneth* hearken; pl.
imperative.
456 *Now have I* now that I
have.

458 *by resoun* in agreement
with the demands of reason.
920 *male* bag, wallet.
921 *fair* fair, good, excellent
—never in Chaucer the weak
word it has now become.
923 *of devocioun* out of piety.

Or ellës taketh pardon as ye wende,
Al newe and fresh at every tounes ende,
So that ye offren alwey newe and newe
Nobles and pens, which that be good and trewe.　930
It is an honour to everich that is heer
That ye mowe have a suffísant pardoneer
Tassoillë you in contree as ye ryde,
For aventúrës which that may bitide.
Peráventure thér may fallen oon or two　935
Doun of his hors and breke his nekke atwo:
Look which a seuretee is it to you alle
That I am in your felawship yfalle,
That may assoillë you bothe more and lasse,
Whan that the soul shal fro the body passe.　940
I redë that our Host here shal biginne,
For he is most envoluped in sinne.
Com forth, sir Host, and offre first anon,
And thou shalt kiss the relikes everichon,
Ye, for a grote. Unbokel anon thy purs."　945
" Nay, nay," quod he, " than have I Cristës curs!
Let be," quod he, " it shal not be, so theech!
Thou woldest make me kiss thyn oldë breech,
And swere it were a relik of a seint."

This Pardoner answerdë not a word;　956
So wroth he was, no word ne wolde he seye.

" Now," quod our Host, " I wol no lenger pleye
With thee, ne with noon other angry man."

But right anon the worthy Knight bigan,　960

929　*alwey* ' ever afresh.'

930　*Nobles* gold coins, worth 6s. 8d. each.

931　*everich* i.e. ever each, everyone.

932　*a suffisant* ' a pardoner who is able to absolve you as you ride along the countryside.'

934　*For aventures* because of mishaps.

937　*which* ' what a security.'

939　*bothe* ' both more and less, richer and poorer.'

941　*rede* counsel, suggest.

942　*envoluped* enveloped, involved.

946　*than* ' then may I have.'

947　*so theech*＝so thee ich as I hope to thrive.

948　*breech* breeches.

958　*lenger* longer.

Whan that he saw that al the peple lough :
" No more of this ! for it is right ynough.
Sir Pardoner, be glad and mery of chere ;
And ye, Sir Host, that been to me so dere,
I prey you that ye kiss the Pardoner ;   965
And, Pardoner, I prey thee, draw thee neer,
And, as we diden, let us laugh and pleye."
Anon they kiste, and riden forth hir weye.

The Wife's Preamble (or the Prologue of the Wife of Bath's Tale)

D

" Experience, though noon auctoritee
Were in this world, were right ynough to me
To speke of wo that is in mariage ;
For, lordinges, sith I twelf yeer was of age
(Thanked be God, that is eterne on live),   5
Housbondes at chirchë door I have had five ;
For I so oftë have ywedded be ;
And alle were worthy men in hir degree.
But me was told certein, not longe agon is,
That sith that Crist ne went never but onis   10
To wedding, in the Cane of Galilee,
That by the same ensample taught he me
That I ne sholdë wedded be but ones.
Herk eek, lo ! which a sharp word for the nones
Beside a wellë Jesus, God and man,   15
Spak in repreve of the Samaritan :
' Thou hast yhad five housbondës,' quod he ;
' And that ilk man, the which that hath now thee,

---

1 *auctoritee* written authority, authoritative statement.

5 *is* ' lives eternally.'

6 *at chirche door :* the priest formerly joined the hands of the couple at the church door. Cp. Prologue A.460.

8 *degree* position, rank.

9 *not* ' not long ago.'

10 *onis* once.

11 *the Cane* Cana (John ii. 1).

14 *Herk* hark, hearken.

16 *repreve* reproof (John iv. 18).

18 *thilke=the ilke* the same, that.

Is noght thyn housbond ' : thus seide he certein.
What that he ment therby I can not seyn,   20
But that I axe, why that the fifthë man
Was noon housbond to the Samaritan.
How many might she have in mariage ?
Yet herde I never tellen, in myn age,
Upon this nombre diffiniciöun :   25
Men may devine, and glosen up and doun,
But wel I woot expres, withoutë lye,
God bad us for to wex and multiplye ;
That gentil text can I wel understonde ;
Eek wel I woot he seidë, myn housbonde   30
Sholde letë fader and moder and takë me :
But of no nombre menciöun made he,
Of bigamye or of octogamye.
Why sholdë men speke of it vileinye ?
Blessëd be God that I have wedded five ;
Welcome the sixtë whan that ever he shal !   45
For sothe I wol not kepe me chaste in al ;
Whan myn housbond is fro the world ygon,
Som Cristen man shal weddë me anon ;
For than thapostle seith that I am free
To wedde, a Goddes half, where it liketh me.   50
He seith that to be wedded is no sinne :
' Bét is to be wedded than to brinne.'

---

21 *that I axe* I ask this.
24 *age* lifetime.
25 'A precise statement of this number.'
26 *devine* ' guess, and write copious commentaries.'
27 *expres* positively.
28 *wex* wax, increase (Gen. i. 28).
29 *gentil* noble, excellent.
31 *lete* leave (Matt. xix. 5).
33 *bigamye*. Not only in Canon Law, but in general usage, this word formerly meant the marrying of two women in succession (the Wife extends it to two husbands): *octogamye* marrying eight husbands in succession.
34 *vileinye* language unworthy of a gentleman.
45 *shal* sc. " come."
46 *in al* altogether.
50 *a Goddes half* " de la part de Dieu," in God's name (1 Cor. vii. 39).
52 *brinne* burn (1 Cor. vii. 28, 29).

What rekketh me though folk say vileinye
Of shrewëd Lameth and his bigamye ?
I woot wel Abraham was an holy man,　　　　55
And Jacob eek, as ferforth as I can ;
And ech of hem hadde wivës mo than two,
And many another holy man also.
Where can ye say, in any maner age,
That highë God defended mariage　　　　60
By expres word ?　I pray you, telleth me ;
Or where comanded he virginitee ?
I woot as wel as ye, it is no drede,
Thapostle, whan he speketh of maidenhede,
He seide, that precept therof hadde he noon.　　　65
Men may conseille a womman to been oon,
But conseilling is no comandëment ;
He put it in our ownë juggëment.
For haddë God comanded maidenhede,
Than hadde he dampnëd wedding with the dede ;　70
And certes, if ther were no seed ysowe,
Virginitee wherof than sholde it growe ?
Poul dorstë not comanden attë leeste
A thing of which his maister yaf noon heeste.
The dart is set up for virginitee ;　　　　75
Cacche whoso may, who renneth best lat see.

---

53 *What rekketh me* what
recks it me ? what do I care ?

54 *shrewed* accursed (Gen.
iv. 19) : *bigamye* used here in
the modern sense of having two
wives at once.

56 *as ferforth as I can* as far
as I know.

59 *in any maner age* in any
kind of age—a common con-
struction.

60 *defended* forbad.

61 *expres* definite, explicit.

63 *it is no drede* without
doubt.

65 1 Cor. vii. 25.

66 *to been oon* to remain
single.

70 ' Then in doing so he
would have condemned mar-
riage.'

73 *Poul* St. Paul : *atte leste*
at least, certainly.

74 *heeste* command, behest.

75–6 ' The prize is offered for
virginity ; win it who may.' Cp.
1 Cor. ix. 24.　Tyrwhitt quotes
from Lydgate's *Falls of Princes* :
" And oft it happeneth, he that
　　hath best ron
Doth not the spere, like his
　　desert, possede."

But this word is not taken of every wight,
But theras God list yive it of his might.
I woot wel that thapostle was a maide ;
But natheles, though that he wroot and saide   80
He wolde that every wight were such as he,
Al nis but conseil to virginitee ;
And, for to been a wyf, he yaf me leve
Of índulgence ; so it is no repreve
To weddë me, if that my makë dye,   85
Withoute excepciöun of bigamye,
Al were it good no womman for to touche
(He mente as in his bed or in his couche) ;
For peril is bothe fyr and tow tassemble ;
Ye knowe what this ensample may resemble.   90
This is al and som, he heeld virginitee
More profiteth than wedding in freletee
(Freletee clepe I, but-if that he and she
Wolde leden al hir lyf in chastitee).
I graunte it wel, I havë noon envye   95
Though maidenhede preferrë bigamye ;
Hem liketh to be clenë, body and goost.
Of myn estaat I nil not make no boost ;
For wel ye knowe, a lord in his houshold
Ne hath not every vessel al of gold ;   100

77–8 'But this word does not apply to everybody, only where it pleases God in his might to bestow [the power to remain single].'

79 *a maide* celibate.

80 *wroot* wrote (1 Cor. vii. 7).

82 *conseil* 'counsel to remain single.'

84 *Of indulgence* 1 Cor. vii. 6 : "Hoc autem dico *secundum indulgentiam* " (But I speak this by permission).

84–6 'so, if my husband die, it is no reproach to wed me, not even on the ground of bigamy.'

88 *He* St. Paul, in 1 Cor. vii. 1.

89 *fyr* ' to bring together fire and tow.'

91 *al and som* the whole matter.

92 *freletee* frailty.

93 *but-if that* unless.

95 *I graunte it wel* I readily agree.

96 *preferre* is superior to, preferable to.

97 *Hem liketh* it pleases them (who remain single) : *goost* spirit.

98 *estaat* state (of marriage) : *nil* will not : *boost* boast.

Somme been of tree, and doon hir lord servise.
God clepeth folk to him in sondry wise,
And everich hath of God a propre yifte,
Som this, som that, as that him liketh shifte.
Virginitee is greet perfecciöun,   105
And continence eek with devociöun.
But Crist, that of perfecciöun is welle,
Bád not every wight he sholde go selle
Al that he hadde and yive it to the pore,
And in such wisë folwe him and his fore.   110
He spak to hem that wolde live parfitly ;
And, lordings, by your leve, that am not I."

  Up sterte the Pardoner, and that anon :
" Now, Dame," quod he, " by God and by Seint John !
Ye been a noble prechour in this cas.   165
I was about to wedde a wyf, allas !
What sholde I bye it on my flesh so dere ?
Yet hadde I lever wed no wyf to-yere."

  " Abide," quod she, " my tale is not bigonne.
Nay, thou shalt drinken of another tonne,   170
Er that I go, shal savoure wors than ale.
And whan that I have told thee forth my tale
Of tribulaciöun in mariáge,
Of which I am expert in al myn age
(Thís to seyn, myself have been the whippe),   175
Than mayst thou chesë whether thou wolt sippe
Of thilkë tonnë that I shal abroche.
Be war of it, er thou to ny approche,

---

101 *tree* wood (2 Tim. ii. 20).
103 *a propre yifte* a peculiar, particular, gift (1 Cor. vii. 7).
104 *as that* ' as it pleases Him to ordain, *or* assign them.'
110 *fore* track, steps, footsteps (Matt. xix. 21).
112 *that* one of " them that would live perfectly."
163 *sterte* started.

167 *bye it* pay for it : *dere* dearly.
168 *to-yere* this year ; cp. to-day.
171 *shal savoure* which will taste.
174 *age* life.
175 *This* this is, that is.
177 *abroche* broach.
178 *to ny* too nigh.

For I shal telle ensamples mo than ten.
' Whoso that nil be war by othere men,　　　180
By him shul othere men corrected be : '
The samë wordes writeth Ptholomee ;
Rede in his Almageste, and take it there."

　　" Dame, I wolde praye you, if your wil it were,"
Seydë this Pardoner, " as ye bigan,　　　185
Telle forth your talë, spareth for no man,
And teche us yongë men of your praktike."

　　" Gládly, sirës, sith it may you like.
But yet I pray to al this companye,
If that I speke after my fantasye,　　　190
As taketh not agrief of that I seye,
For myn ententë is but for to pleye.
　　Now, sirs, now wol I tellë forth my tale.
As ever mote I drinken wyn or ale,
I shal say sooth : tho housbondes that I hadde,　　　195
As three of hem were gode and two were badde.
The three men werë gode and riche and olde ;
The bacoun was not fet for hem, I trowe,
That som men han in Essex at Dunmowe.
I governed hem so wel after my lawe,
That ech of hem ful blisful was and fawe　　　220
To bringë me gay thingës fro the faire ;
They were ful glad whan I spak to hem faire,
For, God it woot, I chidde hem spitously.
　　Now herkneth how I bar me proprely,

---

　180 *be war by* take warning from.

　181 *shul* pl. of *shal*. The Latin, quoted in the margin of the Dd. (Camb.) MS., is clearer : " Qui per alios non corrigitur, alii per ipsum corrigentur." Neither this passage nor that in ll. 326–7 has yet been traced to the " Almagest " of the famous astronomer, Ptolemæus.

　183 *it there* them thence.

　191 *As* ' pray do not take amiss what I say.'

　196 *As* redundant.

　217 *fet* fetched.

　220 *fawe* fain.

　222 *faire* kindly — never ' fairly ' in the deteriorated sense of to-day. The rhyme is to be noted.

　223 *spitously* spitefully.

　224 *proprely* suitably.

Ye wisë wivës that can understonde.
Thus shal ye speke and beren hem on honde ;
For half so boldëly can ther no man
Swerë and lyë as a womman can.
I say not this by wivës that been wise,
But-if it be whan they hem misavise.   230
Ywis a wyf, if that she can hir good,
Shal beren him on hond the cow is wood,
And takë witnesse of hir ownë maide
Of hir assent. But herkneth how I saide :
' Sir, oldë kaynard, is this thyn array ?   235
Why is my neighëborës wyf so gay ?
She is honóurëd overal ther she goth ;
I sitte at hoom, I have no thrifty cloth.
What dostow at my neighëborës hous ?
Is she so fair ? artow so amorous ?   240
What roune ye with our maidë ? Benedicite !
Sir, oldë lechour, lat thy japës be.
And if I have a gossib or a freend,
Withouten gilt, thou chidest as a feend,
If that I walke or pleye unto his hous.   245
Thou comest hoom as dronken as a mous,
And prechest on thy bench with evel preef.

---

226 *beren hem on honde* accuse
them ; cp. l. 232.

229 *by* with reference to.

230 *hem misavise* act im-
prudently.

231 *can* ' knows what is to her
advantage.'

232 *beren* ' make him believe
the bird is mad ' : *cow* chough,
jackdaw. The reference is to the
common story of a bird (a parrot
in the " Arabian Nights ") who
reports a wife's misconduct to
her husband, and has to suffer
for it when the wife, with the aid
of her maid, proves that the bird
is a liar (mad).

234 *Of hir assent* sc. to her
mistress's version.

235 *kaynard* dotard : *thyn
array* how you would have me
dressed.

237 *overal ther* everywhere.

238 *thrifty cloth* clothes suitable (for out-of-doors).

239–40. *dostow* dost thou :
artow art thou—a frequent agglu-
tination.

241 *roune* whisper.

243 *gossib* familiar acquaintance (male here).

244 *feend* fiend.

245 *walke or pleye unto* walk
to or amuse myself at.

247 *evel preef* false charges.

Thou sayst to me, it is a greet meschief
To wedde a pourë womman, for costáge ;
And if that she be riche, of heigh paráge,   250
Than seistow that it is a tormentrye
To suffre hir pride and hir malencolye ;
And if that she be fair, thou verray knave,
Thou sayst that every holour wol hir have :
She may no while in chastitee abide   255
That is assailëd upon ech a side.

Thou sayst, some folk desire us for richesse,
Somme for our shape, and somme for our fairnesse ;
And som, for she can either sing or daunce,
And som for gentillesse and daliaunce,   260
Som for hir handes and hir armës smale :
Thus goth al to the devel by thy tale.

Thou sayst, men may not kepe a castel wal,
It may so longe assailed been overal.
And if that she be foul thou sayst that she   265
Covéiteth every man that she may se,
For as a spaynel she wol on him lepe,
Til that she findë som man hir to chepe ;
Ne noon so grey goos goth ther in the lake
As, sayest thou, wol be withoutë make ;   270
And sayst, it is an hard thing for to welde
A thing that no man wol, his thankës, helde.
Thus saystow, lorel, whan thou gost to bedde,
And that no wys man nedeth for to wedde,

---

248 *meschief* misfortune,
trouble.

249 *for costage* because of
expense.

250 *parage* family, birth.

251 *seistow* sayst thou : *a
tormentrye* torture.

253 *fair* beautiful.

254 *holour* rake.

259 *And som* ' and one *is
desired* because.'

260 *gentillesse* gentleness,
good breeding : *daliaunce*
friendly converse.

264 *overal* everywhere.

266 *Coveiteth* desires sinfully.

267 *spaynel* spaniel.

268 *hir to chepe* to bargain
with her.

271-2 *it is an hard* ' it is
difficult to control what no one
will willingly keep.'

273 *lorel* scamp.

Ne no man that entendeth unto hevene.   275
With wildë thonder-dint and firy levene
Motë thy welkëd nekkë be tobroke !
Thou sayst that dropping houses and eek smoke
And chiding wivës maken men to flee
Out of hir ownë hous. A ! benedicite !   280
What eileth swich an old man for to chide ?
Thou sayst, we wivës wol our vices hide
Til we be fast, and than we wol hem shewe :
Wel may that be a proverbe of a shrewe.
Thou sayst that oxen, asses, hors, and houndes,   285
They been assayëd at diversë stoundes,
Bácins, lavours, er that men hem bye,
Spoonës and stooles, and al swich housbondrye ;
And so been pottës, clothës, and array ;
But folk of wivës maken noon assay   290
Til they be wedded : oldë dotard shrewe !
And than, saystow, we wol our vices shewe.

    Thou sayst also that it displeseth me
But-if that thou wolt preise my beautee,
And but thou poure alwey upon my face,   295
And clepe me " fairë dame " in every place ;
And but thou make a feste on thilkë day

---

275 *entendeth unto hevene*
directs his mind towards heaven.
276 *thonder-dint* thunder-
stroke : *leven* lightning.
277 *welked* withered : *tobroke* broken in two.
278 *dropping houses* : the
meaning is made clear by passages in Cant. Tales B.2276
and I.631. The former runs :
" three thinges driven a man out
of his hous ; that is to seyn,
smoke, dropping of reyn (rain),
and wikked wives." The latter
quotes a version of Prov. xxvii.
15 : " an hous that is uncovered
and droppinge, and a chidinge

wyf, been like."
281 *for to chide* to make him
chide thus.
283 *fast* safely married.
285 *hors* horses ; we still
retain " sheep, swine, deer," as
plurals.
286 *assayed* proved, tested :
stoundes times, seasons.
287 *lavours* lavers, vessels for
washing *or* water-jugs.
288 *housbondrye* household
articles.
289 *array* dress, attire.
295 *but thou poure* if thou
wilt not pore.

That I was born, and make me fresh and gay ;
And but thou do to my noríce honóur,
And to my chamberere withinne my bour,   300
And to my fadres folk and his allyes :
Thus saystow, oldë barel ful of lyes !
    And yet of our apprentice Janëkyn,
For his crisp heer shining as gold so fyn,
And for he squiereth me bothe up and doun,   305
Yet hastow caught a fals suspecioün :
I wol him not, though thou were deed tomorwe.
    But tel me this, why hidestow, with sorwe,
The keyës of thy cheste awey fro me ?
It is my good as wel as thyn, pardee.   310
What ! wenestow make an idiot of our dame ?
Now, by that lord that called is Seint Jame,
Thou shalt not bothë, though thou werë wood,
Be maister of my body and of my good ;
That oon thou shalt forgo, maugree thine yën !   315
What nedeth thee of me to enquere or spyen ?
I trowe, thou woldest loke me in thy chiste.
Thou sholdest sayë : " Wyf, go wher thee liste ;
Taak your disport, I wol not leve no talis ;
I knowe you for a trewë wyf, Dame Alis."   320
We love no man that taketh kepe or charge
Wher that we goon ; we wol been at our large.
Of allë men yblessed moot he be,

---

299 *norice* nurse.

300 *chamberere* (lady's) maid :
bour bower, women's apartment.

301 *allyes* relatives.

306 *hastow* hast thou.

307 *I wol him not* I don't
want him.

308 *with sorwe* an impreca-
tion : ' ill luck to thee ! '

310 *good* property, wealth.

311 ' What ! dost thou want
(lit. ween) to make an idiot of
me ? '

312 *that lord* ' St. James, the
apostle.'

315 *That oon* the one, one of
them : *maugree thin yën* in spite
of thine eyes, in spite of all thou
canst do.

316 ' What need is there for
thee to inquire or spy about me ? '

317 *loke* lock.

318 *thee liste* it may please
thee.

319 *leve* believe.

321 *charge* particular care.

The wise astrologien, Dan Ptholome,
That saith this proverbe in his Almageste :   325
" Of allë men his wisdom is highést
That rekketh never who hath the world in honde."
By this proverbë thou shalt understonde :
Have thou ynough ; what thar thee rekke or care
How merily that other folkës fare ?   330
He is to greet a nigard that wol werne
A man to lighte his candle at his lanterne ;
He shal have never the lassë light, pardee !   335
Have thou ynough, thee thar not pleine thee.

Thou sayst also, that if we make us gay
With clothing and with preciöus array,
That it is peril of our chastitee ;
And yet, with sorwe, thou most enforcë thee,   340
And say thise wordës in thapostles name :
" In habit maad with chastitee and shame
Ye wommen shul apparaille you," quod he,
" And not in tressëd heer, and gay perree,
As perlës, ne with gold, ne clothes riche."   345
After thy text, ne after thy rubriche,
I wol not wirche as muchel as a gnat.
Thou seidest this : that I was lyk a cat ;
For whoso woldë senge a cattës skin,
Than wolde the cat wel dwellen in his inn ;   350
And if the cattës skin be slyk and gay,
She wol not dwelle in housë half a day ;

---

329 *what thar thee recche* why
needest thou reck.

333 *to greet* too great : *werne*
refuse.

336 *pleine thee* complain.

340 *yet* moreover : *enforce
thee* strengthen thy case (by
apostolic authority).

342 1 Tim. ii. 9 .

344 *perree* (O. Fr. *pierrie*)
precious stones.

346 *After* in accordance with :
rubriche rubric : the Wife will
obey neither the apostle's command (l. 342) nor her husband's
gloss upon it (l. 337).

347 *wirche* work, do.

349 *whoso* if anyone : *senge*
singe.

350 *wel* ' certainly remain at
home.'

351 *slyk* sleek.

D

But forth she wol er any day be dawed
To shewe her skin, and go a-caterwawed :
This is to say, if I be gay, Sir shrewe,   355
I wol renne out my borel for to shewe.
Sir oldë fool, what eileth thee to spyen ?
Though thou preye Argus with his hundred yën
To be my wardëcors, as he can best,
In feith, he shal not kepe me, but me lest :   360
Yet coude I make his berd, so moot I thee !
    Thou saydest eke, that ther been thingës three,
The whichë thingës troublen al this erthe,
And that no wight ne may endure the ferthe.
O leve Sir shrewë, Jesu shorte thy lyf !   365
Yet prechestow and sayst, an hateful wyf
Yrekened is for oon of thise meschances.
Been ther none other maner resemblances
That ye may liken your parábles to,
But-if a sely wyf be oon of tho ?   370
Thou liknest eek wommanës love to helle,
To barein lond, ther water may not dwelle ;
Thou liknest it also to wildë fyr :
The more it brenneth, the more it hath desyr
To consumen every thing that brent wol be.   375
Thou sayst that, right as wormës shende a tree,
Right so a wyf destroyeth hir housbonde ;
This knowë they that been to wivës bonde.'

---

353   *be dawed* dawn.
354   *go* 'go a caterwauling.'
See note on C.406.
356   *borel* clothes, garments.
359   *wardecors* bodyguard.
360   *but me lest* unless it pleases me (that he should).
361   *coude I* 'I could hoodwink him, as I hope to thrive.'
362-7   See Prov. xxx. 21-23.
364   *no wight* no person, no one : *ferthe* fourth.
366   *prechestow* preachest thou.

367   *Yrekened* reckoned.
370   'Without a poor innocent woman being one of those.'
371-3   Cp. Prov. xxx. 16.
372   *dwelle* remain, lie.
373   *wilde fyr* a composition of highly inflammable substances, readily ignited and very difficult to extinguish, used in warfare, etc.—*N.E.D.*
374   *brenneth* burns.
376   *shende* injure, destroy.
378   *bonde* bound.

Lordings, right thus as ye have understonde,
Bar I stifly myn olde housbondes on honde,   380
That thus they seiden in hir dronkenesse :
And al was fals ; but that I took witnesse
On Janëkin, and on my nece also.
O Lord ! the peine I did hem and the wo,
Ful giltëlees, by Goddës swetë pine !   385
For as an hors I coudë bite and whine ;
I coudë pleine, though I were in the gilt,
Or ellës oftentime hadde I been spilt.
Whoso that first to millë comth first grint ;
I pleined first, so was our werre ystint.   390
They were ful glad to excusen hem ful blive
Of thing of which they never agilte hir live.
Under that colour hadde I many a mirthe,
For al such wit is yeven us in our birthe ;   400
Deceitë, weping, spinning, God hath yive
To wommen kindëly while they may live.
And thus of o thing I avauntë me :
Atte ende I hadde the bettre in ech degree,
By sleighte, or force, or by som maner thing,   405
As by continuel murmur or grucching.
That madë me that ever I wolde hem chide ;
For though the pope had seten hem biside,   420
I wolde not spare hem at hir ownë bord ;

---

380 ‘ I stoutly made my old
husbands believe.’
382 *but that* ‘ except that I
called as witnesses.”
383 *nece* niece.
385 *ful giltelees* although they
were quite guiltless.
386 *and whine* or, on the
other hand, whine.
387 *pleine* complain, lament.
388 *spilt* put to confusion,
undone.
389 *grint* grinds.
390 *werre ystint* strife ended.

391 *blive* quickly.
392 *agilte hir live* were guilty
in their whole lives.
399 *colour* pretext.
402 *kindely* by nature.
403 *avaunte me* boast.
404 *Atte* at the : *in ech
degree* in every way.
405 *sleighte* trickery, cunning : *by som* ‘ in some way or
other.’
406 *grucching* grumbling.
420 *seten* ‘ sat beside them.’

D

For, by my trouthe, I quitte hem word for word.
As help me verray God omnipotent,
Though I right now sholde make my testament,
I ne owe hem not a word that it nis quit.   425
I broghte it so aboutë by my wit,
That they moste yeve it up, as for the beste,
Or ellës hadde we never been in reste ;
For though he lookëd as a wood leoun,
Yet sholde he faille of his conclusiöun.   430
Than wolde I seye : ' Gode lief, tak keep
How mekely looketh Wilkin, ourë sheep ;
Com neer, my spousë, lat me ba thy cheke ;
Ye sholdë been al pacient and meke,
And han a swetë, spicëd consciënce,   435
Sith ye so preche of Jobës paciënce.
Suffreth alwey, sin ye so wel can preche ;
And, but ye do, certein we shal you teche
That it is fair to have a wyf in pees.
Oon of us two moste bowen, doutëlees ;   440
And sith a man is morë resonable
Than womman is, ye mostë been suffrable.'
Such maner wordës haddë we on honde.   451

  Now wol I speken of my fourthe housbonde.
My fourthë housbonde was a revelour,
This is to seyn, he hadde a paramour ;
And I was yong and ful of ragërye,   455
Stiborn and strong, and joly as a pye.
Wel coude I dauncë to an harpë smale,
And singe, ywis, as any nightingale,

---

422 *quitte*, past of *quyte*, requite, repay.
  425 *that* ' that is not repaid.'
  427 *moste* had to, must.
  429 *leoun* lion.
  430 *conclusioun* object, purpose.
  431   *Gode lief* good husband,
good sir (lit. dear).

433 *ba* ' kiss thy cheek.'
435 *spiced* scrupulous.
440 *bowen* bow, give way.
442 *suffrable* the one to give
way.
451 *on honde* between us.
455 *ragerye* passion.
456 *pye* magpie.

Whan I had dronke a draughte of swetë wyn.
Metellius, the foulë cherl, the swyn,   460
That with a staf birafte his wyf hir lyf,
For she drank wyn : though I hadde been his wyf,
He sholdë not han daunted me fro drinke ;
And, after wyn, on Venus moste I thinke.
But, Lord Crist ! whan that it remembreth me
Upon my youthe and on my jolitee,   470
It tikleth me aboute myn hertë rote.
Unto this day it dooth myn hertë bote
That I have had my world as in my time.
But age, allas ! that al wol envenyme,
Hath me biraft my beautee and my pith :   475
Lat go, farewel ; the devel go therwith !
The flour is goon ; ther is no more to telle ;
The bren, as I best can, now moste I selle
But yet to be right mery wol I fonde.
Now wol I tellen of my fourthe housbonde.   480

    I seye, I hadde in hertë greet despyt
That he of any other had delyt ;
But he was quit, by God ! and by Seint Joce !
I made him of the samë wood a croce.
Not of my body in no foul manere,   485
But certeinly I madë folk such chere,
That in his ownë grece I made him frye

---

460 *Metellius*. The reference to the " De Factis Dictisque
Memorabilibus " of Valerius
Maximus, Book vi., chap. 3,
where this story is found, is
given in the margin of the Ellesmere MS. The same chapter is
quoted from again in ll. 643 and
647, and again the source is given
in the margin of MS. E.
  462 *though* if.
  463 *daunted* frightened.
  469 *it remembreth me* I re-
member.
  471 *myn herte rote* the root,

bottom, of my heart.
  472 *bote* good.
  474 *envenyme* poison, infect.
  475 *pith* strength.
  477 *flour* usually " flower,"
but here " flour."
  478 *bren* bran.
  479 *fonde* try, endeavour.
  481 *despyt* spite, malice,
scorn, vexation.
  483 *quit* paid out : *Seint
Joce* a Breton saint of the 7th
century.
  484 ' I made a staff for him
of the same wood.'

For anger and for verray jalousye.
By God ! in erthe I was his purgatórie,
For which I hope his soulë be in glorie.   490
For, God it woot, he sat ful ofte and song
Whan that his shoo ful bitterly him wrong.
Ther was no wight, save God and he, that wiste
In many wise how sorë I him twiste.
He deide whan I cam fro Jerusalem   495
And lyth ygrave under the rodë-beem,
Al is his tombë not so curious
As was the sepulcre of him, Dáriús,
Which that Appelles wroghtë subtilly ;
It nis but wast to burie him preciously.   500
Lat him fare wel, God yeve his soulë reste !
He is now in his grave and in his cheste.
   Now of my fifthë housbonde wol I telle.
God lete his soulë never come in helle !
And yet was he to me the mostë shrewe ;   505
That fele I on my ribbës al by rewe.
I trowe I loved him bestë for that he
Was of his lovë daungerous to me.
We wommen han, if that I shal not lye,   515
In this matere a queintë fantasye :
Waitë what thing we may not lightly have,
Therafter wol we crye al day and crave ;

---

491   *song* sang.
492   *wrong* pinched.
494   *twiste* tormented.
495   *deide* died.
496   *ygrave* buried : *rode-beem* rood-beam, a beam supporting the rood, and usually forming the head of a rood-screen.
497   *curious* ornate, elaborate.
498   A note in the margin of the Ellesmere MS. gives the source of this legendary statement : the " Alexandreid," a long Latin poem of about 1200 A.D., in which it is stated that Apelles was a Jewish sculptor.
499   *subtilly* cunningly, skilfully.
500   *nis but wast* is but waste : *preciously* in costly fashion.
502   *cheste* coffin.
505   *moste shrewe* greatest villain.
506   *al by rewe* all in a row, one after another.
514   *daungerous* chary, sparing.
517   *Waite* watch, observe.

Forbede us thing, and that desiren we ;
Presse on us faste, and thannë wol we flee.   520
With daunger, outë we al our chaffare ;
Greet pres at market maketh derë ware,
And to greet cheep is holde at lytel prys ;
This knoweth every womman that is wys.

My fifthë housbonde, God his soulë blesse !   525
Which that I took for love and no richesse,
He somtime was a clerk of Oxenford,
And had left scole, and wente at hom to bord
Wíth my gossib, dwelling in our toun,
God have hir soule ! hir name was Alisoun.   530
She knew myn herte and eek my privëtee
Bet than our parisshe preest, as moot I thee !
To hire biwreyëd I my conseil al ;
For had myn housbonde lokëd over a wal,
Or doon a thing that sholde han cost his lyf,   535
To hire, and to another worthy wyf,
And to my nece, which that I lovëd weel,
I wolde han told his conseil every deel.
And so I did ful often, God it woot,
That made his face ful often reed and hoot   540
For verray shame ; and blamed himself, for he
Had told to me so greet a privëtee.
And so bifel that onës in a Lente
(So oftentimes I to my gossib wente ;
For ever yet I lovëd to be gay,   545
And for to walke in March, Averill, and May,
Fro hous to hous to herë sondry talis),
That Jankin clerk and my gossib Dame Alis

521-3 ' When there is reluc-
tance to buy, we display all our
wares ; a great crowd of buyers
makes things dear, and too great
a bargain is held to be of little
value.'
    527 *somtime* once.
    528 *scole* the university : *at*

hom to bord (noun) to board.
    529 *gossib* gossip, chum.
    530 *Alisoun.* We learn from
l. 804 that this was also the Wife's
name.
    531 *privetee* secrets, secret.
    533 *biwreyed* revealed.
    540 *That* that which.

D

And I myself into the feeldes wente.
Myn housbond was at London al that Lente ;   550
I hadde the bettre leiser for to pleye,
And for to see, and eek for to be seye
Of lusty folk : what wiste I wher my grace
Was shapen for to be, or in what place ?
Therfore I made my visitaciöuns   555
To vigilies and to processiöuns,
To preching eek and to thise pilgrimáges,
To pleyes of miracles and to mariäges,
And wered upon my gayë scarlet gytes.
Thise wormës, ne thise motthës, ne thise mites,   560
Upon my peril, frete hem never a deel ;
And wostow why ? For they were usëd weel.
Now wol I tellen forth what happëd me.
I seye that in the feeldës walkëd we,
Til trewëly we hadde such daliánce,   565
This clerk and I, that, of my purveyánce,
I spak to him and seide him how that he,
If I were widwe, sholdë weddë me.
For certeinly (I sey for no bobánce)
Yet was I never withouten purveyánce   570

---

550   *Myn housbond* the fourth;
Jankin was the fifth.

551   *leiser* leisure.

552   *seye* seen.

553   *lusty* pleasant, joyous,
jocund, gay: *what wiste* ' how
could I tell on whom or where
my favour was destined to
fall ? '

556   *vigilies* ceremonies on the
eve of a festival.

558   *pleyes of miracles* Miracle
and Mystery plays. The latter
were by far the more common ;
but in England the one name,
Miracles, was used for both.

559   ' And had on my gay
scarlet gowns.'

560   Chaucer's usage of *this*,
these, is noteworthy. Sometimes
the meaning is merely " the
above mentioned," as in Cant.
Tales A.673–5. But when no
previous mention has been made,
the meaning is " the often referred to," " the well known "
(l. 557), and probably here
" referred to in a famous passage
in the Bible."

561   ' I say it at my peril, ate
never a bit of them."

562   *wostow* knowest thou.

563   *tellen forth* tell on, go on
telling.

565   *daliance* amorous toying.

566   *of my purveyance* as a
matter of foresight.

569   *bobance* boast.

Of mariäge, nof othere thingës eek.
I hold a mouses herte not worth a leek
That hath but oon hole for to stertë to,
And, if that faillë, thanne is al ydo.
I bar him on honde he hadde enchanted me 575
(My damë taughtë me that soutiltee),
And eek I seide : I mette of him al night
He wolde han slain me as I lay upright,
And al my bed was ful of verray blood ;
But yet I hope that he shal do me good, 580
For blood betokeneth gold, as me was taught.
And al was fals, I dremed of it right naught ;
Bút I folwed ay my damës lore
As wel of this as of other thingës more.

But now, sir, lat me see what I shal seyn. 585
Aha ! by God ! I have my tale ageyn.
Whan that my fourthë housbond was on bere,
I weep algate and madë sory chere,
As wivës moten, for it is usage,
And with my kerchief coverëd my visage ; 590
But, for that I was purveyed of a make,
I wepte but smal ; and that I undertake.
To chirchë was myn housbond born amorwe
With neighëbores that for him maden sorwe ;
And Jankin, ourë clerk, was oon of tho. 595

---

571 *nof* nor of.
572 A proverb, into which Chaucer's mouse's *heart* is an intrusion : ' I hold that mouse's chance to be worth nothing.'
574 *is al ydo* all is done, all is over.
575 *enchanted* bewitched with a love-potion.
576 *dame* mother : *soutiltee* device, dodge.
577 *mette* dreamt.
578 *upright* asleep on my back.

585 *sir* the Host.
587 *bere* his bier.
588 *weep*. Both this strong form and the weak *wepte* (l. 592) are found in the best MSS. : *algate* all the time.
589 *moten* must.
591 *purveyed of a make* provided with a mate.
592 *but smal* but little : *undertake* warrant.
593 *amorwe* on the morrow.
594 *With* by.

As help me God ! whan that I saw him go
After the bere, me thoughte he hadde a paire
Of leggës and of feet so clene and faire,
That al myn herte I yaf unto his hold.
He was, I trowe, a twenty winter old,   600
And I was fourty, if I shal say sooth ;
But yet I hadde alwey a coltes tooth.
Gat-tothed I was, and that bicam me weel ;
I hadde the prente of seïnt Venus seel.
As help me God ! I was a lusty oon,   605
And fair and riche and yong, and wel bigon ;
For certës I am al Venerien
In feeling, and myn herte is Marcien.   610
Venus me yaf my lust, my likerousnesse,
And Mars yaf me my sturdy hardinesse.
Myn áscendent was Taur, and Mars therinne.
Allas ! allas that ever love was sinne !
I folwed ay myn inclinaciöun   615
By vertu of my constellaciöun ;
For, God so wis be my savaciöun !   621
I ne lovëd never by no discreciöun,
But ever folwedë myn appetit,
Al were he short or long, or blak or whyt ;

---

597 *me thoughte* it seemed to me.

599 *yaf* gave.

603 *Gat-tothed* either (1) goat-toothed, i.e. lascivious, a meaning admirably suiting this passage ; or (2) gate-toothed, gap-toothed, with gaps between the teeth ; but could " that become her well " ? Cp. Prol. A.468.

604 ' I had the impress of Saint Venus's seal.'

606 *wel bigon* thoroughly content, merry ; cp. " woe-begone."

609 *Venerien* like Venus.

610 *Marcien* like Mars.

611 *lust* desire, pleasure, joy, love of pleasure : *likerousnesse* wantonness.

612 *hardinesse* boldness.

613 *Myn ascendent* the sign just rising in the east at my birth. This sign was Taurus, which was also called " the mansion of Venus." When Mars was seen in this sign when ascending, it showed the influence of Mars on Venus.—Skeat. See Appendix.

616 *my constellacioun* Taurus.

621 ' For, as certainly as may God be my salvation.'

624 *Al were he* whether he whom I fancied were.

I took no kepe, so that he likëd me,   625
How poore he was, ne eek of what degree.

What sholde I say but, at the monthës ende,
This joly clerk Jankin, that was so hende,
Hath wedded me with greet solempnitee ;
And to him yaf I al the lond and fee   630
That ever was me yeven therbifore ;
But afterward repented me ful sore.
He noldë suffre nothing of my list.
By God ! he smoot me onës on the lyst,
For that I rente out of his book a leef,   635
That of the strook myn erë wex al deef.
Stiborn I was as is a leonesse,
And of my tonge a verray jangleresse ;
And walke I wolde, as I had doon biforn,
From hous to hous, although he had it sworn,   640
For which, he oftentimës woldë preche,
And me of oldë Romain gestës teche :
How he, Simplicius Gallus, lefte his wyf,
And hir forsook for terme of al his lyf,
Noght but for open-heeded he hir say   645
Loking out at his dore upon a day.
Another Romain tolde he me by name,
That, for his wyf was at a someres game
Without his witing, he forsook hir eke.

---

630 *fee* property.

633 *list=lust* what I desired.

634 *ones* once : *list* ear.

635 *For that* because.

636 *of* on account of : *ere
wex* ear became.

638 *jangleresse* chatterer.

640 *although* 'although he
had sworn I should not.'

642 *olde Romain gestes* not
the " Gesta Romanorum," but
' old Roman stories.' See the
note on D.460. The name in
Valerius Maximus is Sulpicius
Gallus.

645 ' Merely because he saw
her bareheaded.' Valerius Maximus has : " Nam uxorem dimisit,
quod eam *capite aperto* foris
versatam cognouerat."

647 *Another Romain* Sem-
pronius Sophus, from the same
chapter in Valerius Maximus.

648 *for* ' because his wife
was at summer sports without
his knowledge.' Valerius has :
" nihil aliud quam *se ignorante
ludos* ausam spectare."

D

And than wolde he upon his Bible seke   650
That ilkë proverbe of Ecclesiaste,
Where he comandeth and forbedeth faste,
Man shal not suffre his wyf go roule aboute.
Than wolde he say right thus, withouten doute :
' Whoso that buildeth his hous al of salwes,   655
And priketh his blindë hors over the falwes,
And suffreth his wyf to go seken halwes,
Is worthy to been hanged on the galwes.'
But al for noght ; I settë noght an hawe
Of his proverbës, nof his oldë sawe ;   660
Ne I wolde not of him corrected be.
I hate him that my vices telleth me,
And so do mo, God woot, of us than I.
This made him with me wood al outrely ;
I noldë noght forbere him in no cas.   665
    Now wol I say you sooth, by Seint Thomas !
Why that I rente out of his book a leef,
For which he smoot me so that I was deef.
He hadde a book that gladly, night and day,
For his desport he woldë rede alway ;   670
He clepëd it ' Valerie and Theofraste,'

---

651 Ecclesiasticus xxv. 25 : " Give the water no passage ; neither a wicked woman liberty to gad abroad."

652 *faste* firmly.

655-8. In these four proverbial lines the four-beat rhythm and the sameness of the rhyme will at once be noticed. *salwes* osiers, willows : *falwes* fallows, fallow fields : *halwes* shrines (cp. A.463-6).

659 *I sette* ' I set not the value of a haw on.'

660 *sawe* saw, saying.

663 *mo* more, others (Shak. *moe*), compar. adv., correctly construed here with a genitive pl., *of us*.

664 *wood al outrely* quite utterly mad.

665 *forbere* spare, leave alone.

666 *Seint Thomas* no doubt Thomas à Becket.

670 *desport, disport* (839) amusement, diversion.

671 This was a convenient short title for what (it is evident from l. 681) was an album of extracts chosen from favourite authors.

Valerie Epistola Valerii ad Rufinum " de non ducenda uxore," attributed to Walter Map.

Theofraste. Chaucer is a royal borrower : in this Prologue he borrows chiefly from " Le Roman de la Rose " and from

At whichë book he lough alway ful faste.
And eek ther was somtime a clerk at Rome,
A cardinal, that hightë Seint Jerome,
That made a book again Jovinian ;   675
In whichë book eek ther was Tertulan,
Crisippus, Trotula, and Helowys,
That was abbessë not fer fro Parys ;
And eek the Parables of Salomon,
Ovídes 'Art,' and bookës many oon ;   680
And allë thise were bounden in o volume ;
And every night and day was his custume,
Whan he had leiser and vacaciöun
From other worldly occupaciöun,
To reden on this book of wikked wives.   685
He knew of hem mo legendës and lives
Than been of godë wivës in the Bible ;
For, trusteth wel, it is an impossible
That any clerk wol spekë good of wives,
But-if it be of holy seintës lives,   690
Ne of noon other womman never the mo.
Who peintedë the leoun ? Tel me who.

St. Jerome's " Epistle against
Jovinian." The latter work con-
tains also a long extract from the
" Aureolus Liber de Nuptiis "
by Theophrastus, from which
extract Chaucer borrowed freely
between ll. 221 and 306. All
these borrowings are set forth
in detail in Skeat's great Oxford
Press edition.

674 *cardinal* may be freely
rendered here ' one of the fathers
of the church ' : *highte* was or is
called.

676 *book* the reference is to
the " book " of l. 669, not that
of l. 675. *Tertulan* Tertullian,
who wrote a treatise " De
Exhortatione Castitatis."

677 *Crisippus* Chrysippus,

mentioned in St. Jerome's work :
Trotula not identified : *Helowys*
the famous Héloïse (Eloisa),
married to Abelard.

678 *not fer fro Parys* at
Nogent-sur-Seine.

679 *Parables* the Book of
Proverbs.

680 *Ovides " Art "* the " Ars
Amandi."

688 *impossible* sc. thing.

691 ' Never of any other
woman (than saints).'

692 ' Who painted the lion ? '
Not the lion, but the man. So,
who depicted women ? Clerks.
The result would have been very
different if women had been the
writers. The reference is to
Æsop's fable of The Man and the

By God ! if wommen haddë writen stories,
As clerkës han withinne hir oratóries,
They wolde han writen of men more wikkednesse   695
Than al the mark of Adam may redresse.
The children of Mercúrie and Venús
Been in hir wirking ful contrarius ;
Mercúrie loveth wisdom and science,
And Venus loveth riot and dispence ;   700
And, for hir diverse disposicióun,
Ech falleth in others exaltacióun ;
And thus, God woot, Mercúrie is desolat
In Pisces, wher Venús is exaltat ;
And Venus falleth ther Mercúrie is reised ;   705
Therfore no womman of no clerk is preised.
The clerk, whan he is old, and may noght do
Of Venus werkës worth his oldë sho,
Than sit he doun and wryt in his dotage.
That wommen can not kepe hir mariäge.   710
  But now to purpos why I toldë thee
That I was beten for a book, pardee !
Upon a night Jankin, that was our sire,

Lion ; see " The Fables of Æsop," ed. Joseph Jacobs (London, 1889), II. 121. See also Addison and Steele's "Spectator," No. 11.

696 *mark* race.

697 ' Clerks and women respectively.'

698 *contrarius* contrary, opposed.

700 *dispence* lavish spending.

701 *for hir* because of their.

702–5. ' Each falls in the " exaltation " of the other.' There is a Latin note in the margin of the Ellesmere MS., which means : the sign which is the " exaltation " of one planet (in which that planet has greatest influence) is the " depression " of another, which there has least influence ; and the sign of a planet's " depression " is the one opposite to that of its " exaltation." Thus Mercury is " depressed " in Pisces, where Venus is " exalted " ; Venus falls where Mercury is raised, *i.e.* in Virgo, the sign opposite to Pisces. See the Appendix.

708 ' Anything worth his old shoe in the service of Venus.'

709 *sit* sits : *wryt* writes.

710 *kepe* ' be faithful in marriage.'

711 *to purpos why I tolde thee* (the Host) : a characteristically roundabout way of saying, ' Now I come to the reason why Jankin struck me ' (l. 668).

713 *our sire* my husband, the master of the house.

Redde on his book, as he sat by the fire,
Of Eva first, that for hir wikkednesse   715
Was al mankindë broght to wrecchednesse ;
For which that Jesu Crist himself was slain,
That boghte us with his hertë blood again.
Lo ! here expres of womman may ye finde,
That womman was the los of al mankinde.   720
Tho redde he me how Sampson lost his heres ;
Sleping, his lemman kitte hem with hir sheres ;
Thúrgh which treson loste he bothe his yën.
Tho redde he me, if that I shal not lyen,
Of Hercules and of his Dianyre,   725
That causëd him to set himself afire.
Nothing forgat he the penaunce and wo
That Socrates had with his wives two.
Of Clitermistra, for hir lecherye
That falsly made hir housbond for to dye,
He redde it with ful good devociöun.
He tolde me eek for what occasiöun   740
Amphiorax at Thebës loste his lyf :
Myn housbond hadde a legende of his wyf,

---

715 ' Of Eve first, because
of whose wickedness.' The following examples are mainly
taken from works already mentioned in the notes on ll. 460,
642, 671.

717 *that* redundant.

718 *boghte . . . again* re-
deemed.

719 *expres* explicitly re-
corded.

720 *los* ruin.

722 *his lemman kitte* his paramour cut.

725 *Dianyre* Deianira.

728 *wives two.* Chaucer
meant Xanthippe and Myrto.
Plutarch states, in his " Life of
Aristides," that Aristotle (in a

work of doubtful authenticity)
and two other ancient authorities
relate that Myrto, a grand-
daughter of Aristides, became
the wife of Socrates. He was
already married to Xanthippe,
but took pity on Myrto because
she could not get a husband
owing to her extreme poverty.
This story was convincingly re-
futed by Panætius in his " Life
of Socrates."

737 *Clitermistra* Clytemnes-
tra : *lecherye* wantonness.

740 *occasioun* cause.

741 *Amphiorax* Amphiaraus
(French scribes wrote -*x* for
final -*us*.)

Eriphilem, that for an ouche of gold
Hath prively unto the Grekës told
Wher that hir housbond hidde him in a place ;   745
For which he hadde at Thebës sory grace.
Of Lyma tolde he me, and of Lucye ;
They bothë made hir housbondes for to dye :
That oon for love, that other was for hate ;
Lyma hir housbond, on an even late,   750
Empoisoned hath, for that she was his fo ;
Lucia, likerous, loved hir housbond so,
That, for he sholde alwey upon hir thinke,
She yaf him such a maner lovë-drinke
That he was deed, er it were by the morwe :   755
And thus algatës housbondës han sorwe.
Than tolde he me how oon Latumius
Compleined unto his felawe Arrius,
That in his gardin growëd such a tree,
On which, he seide, how that his wivës three   760
Hangëd hemself for hertë despitus.
' O levë brother,' quod this Arrius,
' Yif me a plante of thilkë blissed tree,
And in my gardin planted shal it be.'
    Of latter date, of wivës hath he red,   765

---

743 *Eriphilem* from the "Thebaid" of Statius ; Eriphyle betrayed Amphiaraus for a golden necklace : *an ouche* for *a nouche*, a form which Chaucer also uses ; cp. "an adder " from " a nadder " (Ger. Natter).

746 *sory grace* a stroke of ill luck, as he was forced to go to the siege of Thebes, and was there engulfed by an earthquake.

747 *Lyma* a mistake for *Livia*, who poisoned her husband Drusus ; see Ben Jonson's " Sejanus," II. i : *Lucye* Lucilia, wife of Lucretius ; see Tennyson's poem, " Lucretius."

750 *on an* ' late one evening.'

751 *fo* foe.

752 *likerous* amorous to excess.

753 *for* in order that.

755 *er* ' ere morning.'

756 *algates* in every way.

757 This widespread story with varying names has been traced to Cicero's " De Oratore " —and Cicero no doubt got it from someone else.

761 *for* ' out of jealousy.'

763 *blissed* prob. ' blessed,' but possibly ' happy.' The distinct words *bliss* and *bless* seem to have been confused in Chaucer's day.

765 *latter* later.

That somme han slain hir housbondes in hir bed ;
And somme han driven nailës in hir brain
Whil that they slepte, and thus they han hem slain ;   770
Somme han hem yeven poisoun in hir drinke :
He spak more harm than hertë may bithinke.
And therwithal he knew of mo proverbes
Than in this world ther growen gras or herbes.
' Bet is,' quod he, ' thyn habitaciöun   775
Be with a leoun or a foul dragoun
Than with a womman using for to chide.'
' Bet is,' quod he, ' high in the roof abide
Than with an angry wyf doun in the hous ;
They been so wikked and contrarious,   780
They haten that hir housbondes loven, ay.'
He seide a womman cast hir shame away
Whan she cast of her smok ; and forthermo :
' A fair womman, but she be chaast also,
Is lyk a gold ring in a sowës nose.'   785
Who woldë wenë or who wolde suppose
The wo that in myn hertë was, and pine ?
    And whan I saw he woldë never fine
To reden on this cursëd book al night,
Al sodeinly three levës have I plight   790
Out of his book, right as he redde, and eke
I with my fist so took him on the cheke,
That in our fire he fel bakward adoun.
And he up stirte as dooth a wood leoun,

---

769 See the story of Jael and
Sisera in Judges iv.
    772 *bithinke* think of.
    775 *Bet* better ; in origin
bet is the compar. adv., but
Chaucer uses it both as adv. and
as adj. See, in the Apocrypha,
Ecclesiasticus xxv. 16.
    777 *using for to* wont to.
    778-9 Prov. xxi. 9 : " It is
better to dwell in a corner of the
housetop, than with a brawling

woman in a wide house."
    781 *ay* aye, ever.
    783 *of* off, which is only a
stressed form of *of*.
    784. Prov. xi. 22 : " As a
jewel of gold in a swine's snout,
so is a fair woman which is without discretion " : *chaast*, chaste.
    788 *fine* finish, cease.
    790 *plight* plucked.
    791 *right* even.
    794 *stirte* started.

And with his fist he smoot me on the heed, 795
That in the floor I lay as I were deed.
And whan he saw how stillë that I lay,
He was agast, and wolde han fled his way ;
Til attë laste out of my swough I breide.
' O ! hast thou slain me, falsë theef ? ' I seide, 800
' And for my land thus hast thou mordred me ?
Er I be deed, yet wol I kissë thee.'
And neer he cam and knelëd faire adoun,
And seidë : ' Deerë suster Alisoun,
As help me God, I shal thee never smite. 805
That I have doon, it is thyself to wite ;
Foryeve it me, and that I thee biseke '—
And yet eftsones I hitte him on the cheke,
And seidë : ' Theef, thus muchel am I wreke.
Now wol I dye, I may no lenger speke.' 810
But attë laste, with muchel care and wo,
We felle acorded by us selven two :
He yaf me al the bridel in myn hond
To han the governance of hous and lond,
And of his tonge and of his hond also ; 815
And made him brenne his book anon, right tho.
And whan that I hadde geten unto me
By maistrie al the sovërainëtee,
And that he seide : ' Myn ownë trewë wyf,
Do as thee lust the terme of al thy lyf, 820
Keep thyn honóur, and keep eek myn estaat,'
After that day we hadden never debaat.
God help me so, I was to him as kinde
As any wyf from Denmark unto Inde,

---

799 *out of* ' I came to, out of
my swoon.'
803 *neer* nearer : *faire adoun*
down gently, (almost) humbly.
806 *wite* blame.
807 *foryeve* forgive : *biseke*
beseech.
808 *eftsones* once again.

809 *wreke* avenged.
812 *fille* ' fell into accord,
agreement.'
816 ' And I made him burn
his book at once, right then.'
817 *geten* got.
820 *thee lust*=*list* it pleases
thee.

And also trewe ; and so was he to me.   825
I prey to God, that sit in magestee,
So blesse his soulë for his mercy deere !
Now wol I seye my tale, if ye wol heere."

THE WRANGLE BETWEEN THE SUMMONER AND THE FRIAR

The Frerë lough whan he had herd al this.
" Now, dame," quod he, " so have I joye or blis !   830
This is a long preamble of a tale."
    And whan the Somnour herde the Frerë gale,
" Lo ! " quod the Somnour, " Goddës armës two !
A frere wol entremette him evermo.
Lo ! godë men, a flye and eek a frere   835
Wol falle in every dish and eek matére.
What spekestow of preambulaciöun ?
What ! amble, or trot, or pees, or go sit doun ;
Thou lettest our disport in this manére."
    " Ye, wilt thou so, Sir Somnour ? " quod the Frere ; 840
" Now, by my feith, I shal, er that I go,
Telle of a somnour such a tale or two,
That alle the folk shal laughen in this place."
    " Now ellës, Frerë, I bishrewe thy face,"
Quod this Somnóur, " and I bishrewë me,   845
But-if I tellë talës two or three
Of frerës, er I come to Sidingborne,
That I shal make thyn hertë for to morne ;
For wel I woot thy paciënce is goon."
    Our Hostë cridë : " Pees ! and that anoon " ;   850
And seidë : " Let the womman telle hir tale ;
Ye fare as folk that dronken been of ale.

---

825   *also* as.
832   *gale* sing, cry out.
834   *entremette* ' always be interfering.'
837   *preambulacioun* preamble (l. 831).

844   *elles* otherwise, and so you may : *bishrewe* beshrew, curse.
847   *Sidingborne* Sittingbourne.
850   *Pees* peace.

Do, dame, tell forth your tale, and that is best."
  " Al redy, sir," quod she, " right as you lest,
If I have licence of this worthy Frere."   855
  " Yis, dame," quod he, " tell forth and I wol here."

(*Here is the Wife of Bath's Tale.*)

THE WIFE OF BATH-FRIAR LINK

This worthy limitour, this noble Frere,   1265
He made alwey a maner louring chere
Upon the Somnour, but for honestee
No vileins word as yet to him spak he.
But attë laste he seide unto the Wyf :
" Damë," quod he, " God yeve you right good lyf !   1270
Ye han here touchëd, al so moot I thee !
In scolë-matere greet difficultee.
Ye han seid muchel thing right wel, I seye.
But, dame, here as we ryden by the weye
Us nedeth not to speken but of game,   1275
And lete auctoritees, on Goddës name,
To preching and to scolës of clergýe.
And if it likë to this companye,
I wol you of a somnour telle a game.
Pardee ! ye may wel knowë by the name   1280
That of a somnour may no good be said
(I preye that noon of you be evil apaid) :
A somnour is a renner up and doun

1265 *limitour* licensed to beg in a certain district with fixed limits.

1266 ' He cast always a kind of frowning look.'

1267 *honestee* decency, decorum.

1272 ' A matter about which there is much disputation in the schools.'

1273 *muchel* a great.

1276 *auctoritees* authorities, a reference to the Wife's Tale (D.1208–12) : *on* in.

1277 *clergye* learning.

1282 *evil apaid* ill pleased, dissatisfied.

With mandëments for fornicacïoun,
And is ybet at every tounës ende."   1285
  Our Host tho spak : " A ! sir, ye sholde be hende
And curteis, as a man of your estaat ;
In companye we wol have no debaat.
Telleth your tale, and let the Somnour be."
  " Nay," quod the Somnour, " let him sey to me   1290
Whatso him list ; whan it comth to my lot,
By God ! I shal him quiten every grot.
I shal him tellen which a greet honóur
It is to be a flatering limitour ;
And his office I shal him telle ywis."   1295
  Our Host answérdë : " Pees ! no more of this ! "
And after this he seide unto the Frere :
" Tell forth your talë, levë maister dere."

(*Here is the Friar's Tale.*)

(*Here is the Summoner's Tale, the last line of which is*)

My tale is doon ; we been almost at toune.   2294

THE CLERK'S FORELINK

E

" Sir Clerk of Oxenford," our Hostë saide,
" Ye ryde as coy and stille as dooth a maide,
Were newë spoused, sitting at the bord ;
This day ne herde I of your tonge a word.
I trowe ye studie aboutë som sophime ;   5

1284 *mandements* citations or
summonses to appear in the
archdeacon's court ; hence the
name ' Summoner.'

1285 *ybet* beaten.

1287 *estaat* position, condition, rank.

1292 *him* ' repay him every
atom.'

1293 *which* ' how great an
honour ' (ironical).

1295 *office* function, the true
nature of his occupation.

2294 *toune* Sittingbourne.

3 *were* ' just wedded ': *bord*
table.

5 *sophime* sophism, a specious
but fallacious argument.

But Salomon seith : ' Every thing hath time.'
For Goddës sake, as beth of bettre chere ;
It is no timë for to studien here.
Tell us som mery talë, by your fey ;
For what man that is entred in a pley,   **10**
He nedës moot unto the pley assente.
But precheth not, as frerës doon in Lente,
To make us for our oldë sinnës wepe,
Ne that thy talë make us not to slepe.
Tell us som mery thing of aventúres ;   **15**
Your termës, your colóurs, and your figúres,
Keep hem in stoor til so be ye endite
Heigh style, as whan that men to kingës write.
Speketh so plein at this tyme, I you preye,
That we may understondë what ye seye."   **20**
    This worthy clerk benignëly answérde :
" Hostë," quod he, " I am under your yerde ;
Ye han of us, as now, the governance,
And therefore wol I do you obeisánce,
As fer as reson axeth, hardily.   **25**
I wol you telle a talë which that I
Lernëd at Padowe of a worthy clerk,
As provëd by his wordës and his werk.

---

6 *Salomon* Eccles. iii. 1 :
" To every thing there is a
season."

7 *as* has here nearly the force
of " pray."

9 *by your fey* (faith) a mild
oath, ' for mercy's sake.'

14 ' And let not your tale
put us to sleep.'

16 *termes* of philosophy :
colours of rhetoric, fine phrases :
figures of speech.

17 *til so be* until : *endite*
compose.

22 *yerde* yard, rod, control.

24 *obeisance* obedience.

25 *axeth* asks, demands :
hardily undoubtedly.

27 *Padowe* Padua : *clerk*
Petrarch was a clerk in both
senses of the word, priest and
scholar. It is most probable
that Chaucer's statement covers
a visit of his own to Petrarch
near Padua during his Italian
journey of 1373 ; and it is certain
that the Clerk's Tale is taken
from Petrarch's Latin version
of the last story in the " De-
cameron " (l. 40).

28 *As proved* viz. that he
was *a worthy clerk*, a distinguished scholar.

He is now deed and nailëd in his cheste ;
I prey to God, so yeve his soulë reste !   30
Fraunceis Petrark, the laureat poete,
Hightë this clerk, whos rethorykë swete
Enlumined al Itáille of poetrye,
As Liniän dide of philosophye,
Or lawe, or oother art particuler ;   35
But deeth, that wol not suffre us dwellen heer
But as it were a twinkling of an yë,
Hem bothe hath slain ; and allë shul we dye.
But forth to tellen of this worthy man,
That taughtë me this tale, as I bigan,   40
I seye that first with heigh style he enditeth,
Er he the body of his talë writeth,
A proheme, in the which discriveth he
Pemond, and of Salucës the contree ;
And speketh of Apennyn, the hilles hye   45
That been the boundës of West Lumbardye,
And of Mount Vesulus in speciäl,
Wheras the Poo out of a wellë smal
Taketh his firstë springing and his sours,
That estward ay encresseth in his cours   50
To Emel ward, to Ferrare and Venise—
The which a long thing werë to devise ;

---

29 *deed* dead ; Petrarch died
in 1374.
31 *laureat poete.* In 1340
Petrarch accepted the poet's
laurel wreath from the Roman
Senate, and was crowned at
Easter, 1341.
32 *rethoryke* elegant or elo-
quent writing.
33 *Enlumined* illumined : *of*
with.
34 *Linian* Giovanni di Leg-
nano, professor of Canon Law at
Bologna, where he died in 1383
(l. 38).

43 *proheme* proem ; in reality,
the first part of the tale.
44 *Pemond* Piedmont : *Sa-
luces* Saluzzo.
47 *Mount Vesulus* Monte
Viso, west of Saluzzo, in the
Cottian Alps.
48 *Wheras* where : *welle*
spring.
50 *encresseth* increases.
51 *To Emel ward* towards
Emilia ; see map of Italy, north
of the Etruscan Apennines : *Ferrare* Ferrara : *Venyse* the state
of Venice.

And trewëly, as to my juggëment,
Me thinketh it a thing impertinent,
Save that he wol conveyen his matere.
But this his talë, which that ye may here.   55

(Here is the Clerk's Tale of patient Grisilde.)

LENVOY DE CHAUCER

Grisilde is deed, and eek hir paciënce,
And bothe atonës buried in Itáille ;
For which I crye in open audience :
No wedded man so hardy be tassaille   1180
His wives paciënce in hope to finde
Grisildis, for in certain he shal faille.

O noble wives, ful of heigh prudence,
Lat noon humilitee your tongë naille,
Ne lat no clerk have cause or diligence   1185
To write of you a storie of such merváille
As of Grisildis paciënt and kinde,
Lest Chichivache you swelwe in hir entráille.

Folweth Ekko, that holdeth no silence,
But ever answereth at the countretaille.   1190

---

54 *impertinent* ' irrelevant, except that he wishes to convey his information.'
56 *this* this is.'
1178 *atones* at once, at the same time.
1180 *tassaille* to assail, attack.
1181 *wives* wife's.
1184 *naille* nail.
1185 *diligence* care, heed.
1186 *of such mervaille* so wonderful.

1188 *Chichivache* i.e. *chiche vache*, lean cow, which, according to an old French fable, was lean because its food was patient wives : *swelwe* swallow.
1189 *Folweth* follow, imitate.
1190 *answereth* ' answer back, in retort.' The explanation that one half of a tally (Prol. A.570) " answers " to the other half, the counter-tally, is absurd.

Beth not bidaffëd for your innocence,
But sharply tak on you the governaille.
Emprinteth wel this lesson in your minde
For comune profit, sith it may availle.

Ye archiwives, stondeth at defence ;   1195
Sin ye be strong as is a greet camáille,
Ne suffreth not that men you doon offence.
And, sclendre wivës, fieble as in batáille,
Beth egre as is a tigrë yond in Inde ;
Ay clappeth as a mille, I you consáille.   1200

Ne dreed hem not, do hem no reverence ;
For though thyn housbonde armëd be in maille,
The arwes of thy crabbëd eloquence
Shal perce his brest, and eek his aventáille ;
In jalousie I rede eek thou him binde,   1205
And thou shalt make him couche as dooth a quaille.

If thou be fair, ther folk been in presénce
Shew thou thy visage and thyn appáraille ;
If thou be foul, be free of thy dispence,
To gete thee freendës ay do thy traváille ;   1210
Be ay of chere as light as leef on linde,
And lat him care and wepe and wringe and waille.

1191 *bidaffed* befooled.
1192 *governaille* control of affairs.
1194 *availle* be useful.
1195 *archiwives* masterful wives.
1196 *camaille* camel.
1198 *as* redundant.
1199 *egre* fierce.
1200 *clappeth* chatter, like the constant noise made by the clapper, clap, or clack, of a mill.
1203 *crabbed* showing ill-temper.
1204 *aventaille* ventail, beaver, the lower part of the front of a helmet.
1206 *couche* ' cower, lie close, like a quail.'
1207 *ther* where : *in presence* assembled in numbers
1210 *do thy travaille* labour.
1211 *linde* linden or lime tree ; this alliterative phrase was proverbial.
1212 *wringe* sc. his hands.

The Clerk-Merchant Link

" Weping and wailing, care and other sorwe,
I know ynogh on even and on morwe,"
Quod the Marchant, " and so doon othere mo   1215
That wedded been ; I trowe that it be so ;
For wel I woot it fareth so with me.
I have a wyf, the worstë that may be ;
For though the feend to hir ycoupled were,
She wolde him overmacche, I dar wel swere.   1220
What sholde I you reherce in special
Her heigh malice ? She is a shrewe at al.
Ther is a long and largë difference
Bitwix Grisildis gretë paciënce
And of my wyf the passing crueltee.   1225
Were I unbounden, al so moot I thee !
I woldë never eft comen in the snare.
We wedded men liven in sorwe and care.
Assayë whoso wol, and he shal finde
I seyë sooth, by Seint Thomas of Inde !   1230
As for the morë part, I sey not alle ;
God shildë that it sholdë so bifalle !
A ! good Sir Host, I have ywedded be
Thise monthës two, and morë not, pardee !
And yet, I trowë, he that al his live   1235
Wyfles hath been, though that men wolde him rive

1213 All such repetitions, as this of " care and weep and wail," help to determine the true order of the Tales.

1214 *on even* ' night and morning.'

1215 *othere mo* others.

1221 *in special* in particular.

1222 *at al* altogether, in every respect.

1225 *passing* surpassing, extraordinary.

1226 *al so* a more emphatic *so ;* ' as I hope to thrive.'

1229 *Assaye* make trial, try.

1230 *of Inde* the apostle, possibly to distinguish him from à Becket. His labours in India are mentioned by Jerome.

1231 *As* ' for the most part.'

1232 *shilde* forbid.

1236 *Wyfles* wifeless : *rive* rive, pierce.

Unto the herte, ne coude in no manére
Tellen so muchel sorwe, as I now here
Coude tellen of my wivës cursednesse."
  " Now," quod our Host, " Marchant, so God you
      blesse !   1240
Sin ye so muchel knowen of that art,
Ful hertëly I pray you telle us part."
  " Gladly," quod he ; " but of myn ownë sore,
For sory herte, I tellë may no more."

(Here is the Merchant's Tale of January and his wife May.)

THE MERCHANT-SQUIRE LINKS

" Ey ! Goddës mercy ! " seide our Hostë tho,
" Now such a wyf I pray God kepe me fro.   2420
Lo ! whichë sleightës and subtílitees
In wommen been ! for ay as bisy as bees
Been they, us sely men for to deceive ;
And from a sothë ever wol they weive :
By this Marchantës tale it proveth weel.   2425
But doutëles as trewe as any steel
I have a wyf, though that she poorë be ;
But of hir tonge a labbing shrewe is she ;
And yet she hath an heep of vicës mo ;
Therof no fors, let alle such thingës go.   2430
But wit ye what ? In conseil be it seid,
Me reweth sore I am unto hir teid ;
For, and I sholdë rekenen every vice

E

Which that she hath, ywis I were to nice,
And causë why : it sholde reported be   2435
And told to hir of some of this meynee
(Of whom, it nedeth not for to declare,
Sin wommen connen outen such chaffare) ;
And eek my wit suffiseth not therto,
To tellen al : wherfore my tale is do.   2440

(Thought to mark the beginning of the fourth day.)

Squiér, com neer, if it your willë be,
And sey somwhat of love ; for certës ye
Connen theron as much as any man."
    " Nay, sir," quod he, " but I wol sey as I can
With hertly wil ; for I wol not rebelle   5
Against your lust : a talë wol I telle.
Have me excusëd if I speke amis ;
My wil is good ; and lo ! my tale is this.

(Here is the Squire's Tale.)

THE SQUIRE-FRANKLIN LINK

F

" In feith, Squiér, thou hast thee wel yquit
And gentilly ; I preisë wel thy wit,"
Quod the Frankelein ; " considering thy youthe,   675
So feelingly thou spekest, sir, I allow thee.
As to my doom, ther is noon that is here

2435 *cause why* for this
reason.
2436 *meynee* company.
2437 *Of whom :* no doubt
the Host means by the Wife of
Bath.
2438 *connen* ' know how to
disclose such matters.'
2440 *my tale is do* I have no

more to say about the matter.

3 *Connen* know.
5 *hertly* hearty.
673 *thee* ' quit thyself well.'
674 *gentilly* as befits one of
gentle birth.
676 *allow* commend.
677 *As to* ' in my judgment.'

Of eloquencë that shal be thy pere,
If that thou live. God yevë thee good chaunce,
And in vertu sende thee continuaunce ;   680
For of thy spechë I have greet deintee.
I have a sone, and, by the Trinitee,
I haddë lever than twenty pound-worth lond,
Though it right now were fallen in myn hond,
He were a man of such discreciöun   685
As that ye been ; fy on possessiöun
But-if a man be vertuous withal !
I have my sonë snibbëd, and yet shal,
For he to vertu listeth not entende ;
But for to pleye at dees and to despende   690
And lese al that he hath is his uságe ;
And he hath lever talken with a page
Than to comune with any gentil wight,
Ther he mighte lernë gentillesse aright."

" Straw for your gentillessë," quod our Host.   695
" What ! Frankëlein, pardee ! sir, wel thou wost
That ech of you moot tellen attë leste
A tale or two, or breken his biheste."

" That knowe I wel, sir," quod the Frankëlein ;
" I prey you, haveth me not in desdein   700
Though to this man I speke a word or two."

" Tell on thy tale withouten wordës mo."

" Gladly, Sir Host," quod he, " I wol obeye
Unto your wil ; now herkneth what I seye.
I wol you not contrarien in no wise   705
As fer as that my wittës wol suffise ;

---

678 *pere* peer, equal.
679 *chaunce* luck, fortune.
681 *deintee* delight.
683 *twenty* 'twenty pounds worth of land.'
686 *possessioun* great possessions.
688 *snibbed* reproved (lit. snubbed).

689 *listeth* ' does not choose (care, like) to incline.'
690 *dees* dice: *despende* spend.
693 *gentil* of gentle birth, gentle, noble.
696 *wost* knowest.
698 *biheste* promise.
700 *desdein* disdain.
705 *contrarien* oppose.

G

I prey to God that it may plesen you,
Than woot I wel that it is good ynow."

(*Here is the Franklin's Tale.*)

(*Here is the Second Nun's Tale of St. Cecilia.*)

THE SECOND NUN-CANON'S YEOMAN LINK

G

Whan ended was the lyf of Seint Cecile,
Er we had riden fully fivë mile,   555
At Boghton under Blee us gan atake
A man that clothëd was in clothës blake,
And undernethe he hadde a white surplys.
His hakeney, which that was al pomely grys,
So swattë that it wonder was to see ;   560
It semëd he had prikëd milës three
(The hors eek that his yeman rood upon
So swattë that unnethë mighte it gon) ;
Aboute the peitrel stood the foom ful hye,
He was of foom al flekked as a pye.   565
A malë tweyfold on his croper lay,

---

708 *ynow* enough.

555 *five mile* from Ospringe
(close to Faversham), where was
their hostelry (l. 589) on the
third night : see the Introduc-
tion.

556 *Boghton under Blee*
Boughton-under-Blean   (*i.e.*
Blean Forest ; cp. *the Blee*,
H.3), a village halfway between
Ospringe and Canterbury, five
miles from each : *gan atake*
overtook.

557 *A man* the Canon.

559 *hakeney* hack : *pomely*

grys dapple-grey.

560 *swatte* past of *swete* (579),
to sweat.

561 *priked* ridden hard.

562 *yeman* yeoman, servant.

563 *mighte* ' could it walk.'

564 *peitrel* (originally) armour
for a horse's breast, (here) the
breastpiece of the harness : *foom*
foam.

565 *flekked* ' flecked like a
magpie,' the Canon being dressed
in black (557). Ll. 562–3 alone
refer to the yeoman.

566 ' A twofold wallet lay on
the crupper.'

It semed that he caried lyte array.
Al light for somer rood this worthy man,
And in myn hertë wondren I bigan
What that he was, til that I understood   570
How that his cloke was sowed to his hood ;
For which, whan I had long avised me,
I demëd him som chanoun for to be.
His hat heng at his bak doun by a laas,
For he had riden more than trot or paas ;   575
He had ay prikëd lyk as he were wood.
A clotë-leef he hadde under his hood
For swoot, and for to kepe his heed from hete ;
But it was joyë for to seen him swete.
His forheed droppëd as a stillatórie   580
Were ful of plantain and of paritórie.
And whan that he was come he gan to crye :
" God save," quod he, " this joly companye ! "
Faste have I prikëd," quod he, " for your sake,
Bycausë that I woldë you atake,   585
To ryden in this mery companye."
    His yeman eek was ful of curteisye,
And seidë : " Sirs, now in the morwe tide
Out of your hostelrie I saw you ryde,
And warnëd heer my lord and my soverain,   590

---

568 *Al* ' quite lightly clad for summer.'

570 *understood* realised.

571 *How that* that.

572 *avised me* considered, pondered.

573 The grounds of this inference are not clear, and apparently Chaucer was " long " in doubt. The description agrees with that of the Black Augustinian Canons ' regular,' but the sequel seems to make it clear that this was a ' secular ' Canon (657 *seq.*).

574 *laas* cord.

575 *more* ' faster than a trot or a foot-pace.'

577 *clote-leef* burdock leaf.

578 *For swoot* to prevent sweating. We must infer that only the upper edge of the hood was sewn to his " cloke " (571), and that the hood was turned, as was usual, over the head, with the leaf under it.

580 *as a* ' like a still full of plantain and pellitory.'

588 *morwe tide* morning.

589 *saugh* saw.

590 *warned* told : *heer* ' my lord here, this master of mine.'

Which that to ryden with you is ful fain,
For his disport ; he loveth daliaunce."
   " Freend, for thy warning God yeve thee good
      chaunce,"
Than seide our Host ; " for certes it wolde seme
Thy lord were wys, and so I may wel deme ;   595
He is ful jocund also, dar I leye.
Can he ought telle a mery tale or tweye,
With which he gladë may this companye ? "
   " Who, sir ? my lord ? Ye, ye, withouten lye ;
He can of mirthe and eek of jolitee   600
Not but ynough ; also, sir, trusteth me,
And ye him knewë as wel as do I,
Ye woldë wondre how wel and craftily
He coudë werke, and that in sondry wise.
He hath take on him many a greet emprise,   605
Which were ful hard for any that is here
To bringe aboute, but they of him it lere.
As homely as he ryt amongës you,
If ye him knewe, it wolde be for your prow ;
Ye woldë not forgoon his áqueintaunce   610
For muchel good, I dar leye in baláunce
Al that I have in my possessiöun.
He is a man of heigh discreciöun ;
I warne you wel, he is a passing man."
   " Wel," quod our Host, " I pray thee tell me than : 615
Is he a clerk or noon ? Tell what he is."

---

591   *fain* glad.
592   *daliaunce* light familiar talk.
596   *dar* ' I dare lay a wager ' ; cp. John Silver in "Treasure Island" : " And you may lay to that."
597   *ought* at all, by any means : *tweye* two.
598   *glade may* may gladden.
601   *Not* 'not only enough (but a great deal more).'

603   *craftily* skilfully, cunningly.
605   *emprise* enterprise, undertaking.
607   *but* ' unless they should learn it of him.'
608   *As* ' however familiarly he rides.'
610   *forgoon* forgo.
611   *mochel* = *muchel* much, great : *leye in balaunce* hazard, wager (that you would not).

" Nay, he is gretter than a clerk, ywis,"
Seidë this yeman, " and in wordës fewe,
Host, of his craft somwhat I wol you shewe.
I sey, my lord can such subtílitee   620
(But al his craft ye may not wit at me ;
And somwhat helpe I yet to his werkíng),
That al this ground on which we been ridíng,
Til that we come to Caunterbury toun,
He coude al clenë turne it up-so-doun,   625
And pave it al of silver and of gold."

     And whan this yeman haddë thus ytold
Unto our Host, he seidë : " Benedicite !
This thing is wonder merveillous to me :
Sin that thy lord is of so heigh prudénce,   630
Bycause of which men sholde him reverence,
That of his worship rekketh he so lite :
His oversloppë nis not worth a mite,
As in effect, to him, so mote I go !
It is al baudy and totore also.   635
Why is thy lord so sluttish, I thee preye,
And is of power bettre cloth to beye,
If that his dede acordë with thy speche ?
Tellë me that, and that I thee biseche."

     " Why ? " quod this yeman, " wherto axe ye me ? 640
God help me so ! for he shal never thee.
(But I wol not avowë that I sey,
And therfore keep it secree, I you prey.)
He is to wys, in feith, as I bileve ;

---

619 *craft* occupation.
621 *wit at* learn from.
622 *yet* moreover.
625 *al clene* ' turn it clean upside down.'
629 *wonder* (adv.) wondrously, very.
632 ' That he cares so little for appearances.'
633 *oversloppe* outer garment.

634 *As in effect* in reality :
so ' so may I go !', ' in good sooth.'
635 *baudy* ' dirty and rent (asunder).'
637 ' When he is able to buy better clothes.'
638 *his dede* what he can do.
640 *wherto* wherefore.
642 *avowe* maintain, declare openly.

G

That that is overdoon, it wol not preve 645
Aright ; as clerkës seyn, it is a vice.
Wherfore in that I holde him lewed and nice ;
For whan a man hath overgreet a wit,
Ful oft him happeth to misusen it :
So dooth my lord, and that me greveth sore. 650
God it amende ! I can sey you no more."

"Therof no fors, good yeman," quod our Hoost.
"Sin of the conning of thy lord thou woost,
Tell how he dooth, I prey thee hertely,
Sin that he is so crafty and so sly. 655
Where dwellen ye, if it to tellë be ? "

"In the suburbës of a toun," quod he,
"Lurking in hernës and in lanës blinde,
Wheras thise robbours and thise theves by kinde
Holden hir privee fereful residence, 660
As they that dar not shewen hir presénce ;
So faren we, if I shal sey the sothe."

"Now," quod our Host, "yet let me talke to thee :
Why art thou so discoloured of thy face ? "

"Peter ! " quod he, "God yeve it hardë grace ! 665
I am so usëd in the fyr to blowe,
That it hath chaungëd my colóur, I trowe.
I am not wont in no mirour to prye,
But swinke sore and lernë multiplye.
We blondren ever, and pouren in the fyr, 670

645–6 *preve aright* bear test-
ing. The proverb is found
in various languages : "Omne
nimium vertitur in vitium " (suggested in the margin of MS. E.) ;
"Too much of a good thing."

653 *conning* knowledge, skill.

655 *crafty* clever, skilful :
sly cunning.

658 *hernes* corners.

659 *thise* see note on D.560:
theves by kinde born thieves.

660 *privee* secret : *fereful*
filled with fear.

665 *Peter* by St. Peter : *God*
' bad luck to it, a curse upon it.'

666 *used* accustomed, wont
(668).

669 *swinke* toil : *lerne* ' learn
to multiply,' the technical term
for turning the baser metals into
gold.

670 *blondren* deal blindly and
stupidly, blunder : *pouren* pore,
gaze steadily.

And for al that we faile of our desyr,
For ever we lakken our conclusiöun.
To muchel folk we doon illusiöun,
And borwe gold, be it a pound or two,
Or ten, or twelve, or many sommës mo,   675
And make hem wenen, at the leestë weye,
That of a pound we coudë makë tweye.
Yet is it fals. But ay we han good hope
It for to doon, and after it we grope.
But that sciénce is so fer us biforn,   680
We mowen not, although we had it sworn,
It overtake, it slyt awey so faste.
It wol us maken beggers attë laste."
   Whil this yemán was thus in his talkíng,
This chanoun drough him neer, and herde al thing   685
Which this yemán spak, for suspeciöun
Of mennës speche ever haddë this chanoun ;
For Catoun seith, that he, that gilty is,
Demeth al thing be spoke of him ywis :
That was the cause he gan so ny him drawe   690
To his yemán, to herknen al his sawe.
And thus he seide unto his yeman tho :
" Hold thou thy pees and spek no wordës mo,
For, if thou do, thou shalt it dere abye ;
Thou sclaundrest me here in this companye,   695
And eek discoverest that thou sholdest hide."
   " Ye ? " quod our Host, " tell on, whatso bitide ;

---

672 *lakken* ' fail to achieve a successful issue.'
673 ' We delude, befool, many folk.'
676 *at the* ' at the least.'
680 *fer* ' far ahead of us.'
681 *mowen* can.
682 *slyt* slides.
685 *drough* ' drew nearer.'
688 *Catoun* Chaucer has about a dozen references to Dionysius Cato, who wrote

" Disticha " in the third or fourth century A.D. Tyrwhitt quotes the line translated here : " Conscius ipse sibi de se putat omnia dici."
691 *al* ' all that he was saying.'
694 *it dere abye* pay for it dearly.
695 *sclaundrest* slanderest.
696 *discoverest* revealest.

G

Of al his threting rekkë not a mite."

"In feith," quod he, "no more I do but lite."

And whan this chanoun saw it wolde not be, 700
But his yemán wolde telle his privetee,
He fledde awey for verray sorwe and shame.

"A !" quod the yeman, "here shal arisë game ;
Al that I can anon now wol I telle,
Sin he is goon : the foulë feend him quelle ! 705
For never hereafter wol I with him mete
For peny ne for pound, I you bihete.
He that me broughtë first unto that game,
Er that he dyë, sorwe have hé and shame !
For it is ernest to me, by my feith ; 710
That fele I wel, whatso any man seith.
And yet, for al my smert and al my grief,
For al my sorwe, labour, and meschíef,
I coudë never leve it in no wise.
Now woldë God my wit mightë suffise 715
To tellen al that longeth to that art !
But nathéles you wol I tellen part ;
Sin that my lord is goon, I wol not spare ;
Such thing as that I knowe I wol declare."

(Here is the Canon's Yeoman's Tale.)

THE CANON'S YEOMAN-MANCIPLE LINK

H

Woot ye not where ther stant a lytel toun,
Which that ycleped is Bob-up-and-doun,

---

698 *threting* threatening.

699 *no* ' I care no more than
a little.'

700 *it* ' that his servant would
not obey him.'

703 *A !* ah ! : *arisë game* be
some sport.

705 *quelle* kill.

706 *mete* meet.

707 *bihete* promise.

710 *ernest* a serious matter.

712 *smert* pain.

716 *longeth* belongs.

1 *toun* farm or hamlet.

2 *ycleped* called : *Bob-up-
and-doun* there is a place called
Up-and-down Field at about the

Under the Blee in Caunterbury weye?
Ther gan our Hostë for to jape and pleye,
And seidë: " Sirs, what! Dun is in the mire.   5
Is ther no man, for preyer ne for hire,
That wol awake our felawe al bihinde?
A theef mighte him ful lightly robbe and binde.
See how he nappeth, see, for cokkës bones,
As he wol fallë from his hors at ones.   10
Is that a Cook of Londoun, with meschaunce?
Do him come forth, he knoweth his penáunce,
For he shal telle a talë, by my fey,
Although it be not worth a botel hey.
Awake, thou Cook," quod he, " God yeve thee sorwe!   15
What eileth thee to slepë by the morwe?
Hast thou had fleen al night, or art thou dronke,
Or hast thou al the longë night yswonke,
So that thou mayst not holden up thyn heed?"

This Cook, that was ful pale and nothing reed,   20
Seide to our Host: " So God my soulë blesse,
As ther is falle on me such hevinesse,
Noot I not why, that me were lever slepe
Thán the bestë galoun wyn in Chepe."

---

right distance from Canterbury ;
if this is the same place as
Chaucer's, the Canterbury road
has somewhat changed its course,
as is quite possible.

3   the Blee Blean Forest ; see
G.556.

5   " Dun is in the mire is a
Christmas gambol at which I
have often played. A log of
wood is brought into the midst
of the room : this is Dun (the
cart-horse), and a cry is raised
that he is stuck in the mire. Two
of the company advance, either
with or without ropes, to draw
him out."—W. Gifford. See
" Romeo and Juliet " I. 4. 41.

Thus the Host means : ' Who
will help us out ? '

8   lightly easily.

9   cokkes to avoid mention of
the Deity ; cp. B.3087.

11   with ' bad luck to him.'

12   Do ' make him come for-
ward.'

14   botel hey bottle, bundle,
of hay ; cp. barel ale (B.3083),
galoun wyn (24).

16   by ' in the morning.'

17   fleen fleas.

18   yswonke laboured.

20   reed red.

23   noot know not : me ' I
would rather.'

24   Chepe Cheapside.

H

" Wel," quod the Maunciple, " if it may doon ese 25
To thee, Sir Cook, and to no wight displese
Which that here rydeth in this companye,
And that our Host wol, of his curteisye,
I wol as now excuse thee of thy tale ;
For, in good feith, thy visage is ful pale, 30
Thyn yën daswen eek, as that me thinketh,
And wel I woot thy breeth ful sourë stinketh ;
That sheweth wel thou art not wel disposed ;
Of me, certein, thou shalt not been yglosed.
See how he ganeth, lo ! this dronken wight, 35
As though he woldë swolwe us anonright.
Hold cloos thy mouth, man, by thy fader kin.
The devel of hellë sette his foot therin !
Thy cursëd breeth infectë wol us alle ;
Fy ! stinking swyn, fy ! foulë moot thee falle ! 40
A ! taketh heed, sirs, of this lusty man.
Now, swete sir, wol ye justen attë fan ?
Therto me thinketh ye been wel yshape !
I trowë that ye dronken han wyn ape,
And that is whan men pleyen with a straw." 45
    And with this speche the Cook wex wroth and wraw,

---

25 *doon ese to* please or help.

28 *that* ' if our Host is willing.'

31 *daswen* are dazed : *that* it.

32 *soure* sourly, vilely.

33 *not* ' indisposed.'

34 *yglosed* flattered.

35 *ganeth* yawns.

36 *swolwe* ' swallow us right off.'

40 *foule* ' may things fall out foully for thee,' ' ill betide thee.'

42 *justen* ' ride at the fan, vane, or shield, of the quintain.' A drunken lurch of the Cook may have suggested the tilter stooping to avoid the bag of sand.

43 ' For that it seems to me you are naturally well fitted ! '

44 *wyn ape* ape-wine. The sheep, the lion, the monkey, and the sow were associated with different stages of drunkenness, and also with certain wines that produced, or were supposed to produce, the effects and the behaviour commonly associated with those stages. Skeat quotes Barclay's " Ship of Fools " : " Some are Ape-dronke, full of lawghter and of toyes." The Manciple ironically chaffs the Cook on being thus ' silly drunk,' " whan men pleyen with a straw " ; the sequel shows that he had reached a later stage.

46 *wraw* angry.

And on the Maunciple he gan noddë faste
For lakke of speche, and doun the hors him caste,
Wheras he lay till that men up him took :
This was a fair chiváchee of a Cook !   50
Allas ! he naddë holde him by his ladel.
And er that he again were in his sadel
Ther was greet shouving bothë to and fro
To lifte him up, and muchel care and wo,
So unweeldy was this sory, pallëd gost.   55
    And to the Maunciple than spak our Host :
" Bycausë drink hath dominaciöun
Upon this man, by my savaciöun
I trowe he lewëdly wolde telle his tale ;
For, were it wyn or old or moisty ale   60
That he hath dronke, he speketh in his nose,
And fneseth faste, and eek he hath the pose.
He hath also to do more than ynough
To kepe him and his capel out of slough ;
And if he fallë from his capel eftsone,   65
Than shal we allë have ynough to done
In lifting up his hevy, dronken cors.
Tell on thy tale ; of him make I no fors.
But yet, Maunciple, in feith thou art to nyce
Thus openly repreve him of his vice ;   70
Another day he wol, peráventure,
Reclaimë thee and bringë thee to lure :
I mene, he spekë wol of smalë thinges,
As for to pinchen at thy rekeninges ;

---

50 *chivachee* equestrian feat.
51 *he nadde* ' that he had not stuck to his ladle ! '
54 *care* anxiety, trouble.
55 *palled* enfeebled.
59 *lewedly* ill, amiss.
60 *moisty* fresh, new-drawn.
62 *fneseth* breathes heavily : *the pose* nasal catarrh, cold in the head.

64 *capel* nag.
65 *eftsone* soon after, once again.
68 *make* ' I take no account.'
72 The metaphors are from hawking : *reclaime* call back a hawk to the falconer's wrist : *lure* bait used to this end.
74 *pinchen* ' find fault with thy accounts ' ; it is clear from

That were not honeste, if it cam to preef." 75
   "No," quod the Maunciple, " that were a greet
      mescheef ;
So mighte he lightly bringe me in the snare ;
Yet hadde I lever payen for the mare
Which he ryt on, than he sholde with me strive.
I wol not wratthe him, also moot I thrive ! 80
That, that I spak, I seide it in my bourde ;
And wit ye what ?   I have heer in a gourde
A draught of wyn, ye, of a ripë grape,
And right anon ye shal seen a good jape :
This Cook shal drinke therof, if that I may ; 85
Up pein of deeth, he wol not seye me nay."
   And certeinly, to tellen as it was,
Of this vessel the Cook drank faste, allas !
What neded him ?   He drank ynough biforn.
And whan he haddë pouped in this horn, 90
To the Maunciple he took the gourde again ;
And of that drinke the Cook was wonder fain,
And thankëd him in such wise as he coude.
   Than gan our Host to laughen wonder loude,
And seide :   " I see wel it is necessárie, 95
Wher that we goon, good drink we with us carie ;
For that wol turnë rancour and disese
To acord and love, and many a wrong apese.
O thou, Bacus, yblessed be thy name !
That so canst turnen ernest into game ; 100
Worship and thank be to thy deitee !

Prol. A.567 *seq*. that the Manciple made big profits for himself
in buying for his " temple."
   75 *honeste* to thy credit :
preef the test.
   77 *lightly* readily, easily :
bringe ' lay bare my illicit gains.'
   80 *wratthe* anger : *also* as.
   81 *bourde* jest.
   82 *gourde* bottle.

85 *may* can make him.
86 *Up* upon, on.
90 *pouped* blown, *i.e.* taken
a draught.
91 *took* gave.
96 *Wher that* wherever.
98 *apese* put an end to.
99 *Bacus* Bacchus, god of
wine.

Of that matere ye get no more of me.
Tell on thy talë, Maunciple, I thee preye."
" Wel, sir," quod he, " now herkneth what I seye."

(Here is the Manciple's Tale.)

THE MANCIPLE-PARSON LINK
                                                                    1

By that the Maunciple hadde his tale al ended,
The sonnë from the south line was descended
So lowë that he nas not, to my sighte,
Degreës nine and twenty as in highte.
Four of the clokke it was tho, as I gesse ;   5
For eleven foot, or lytel more or lesse,
My shadwe was at thilkë time, as there,
Of such feet as my lengthë parted were
In six feet equal of proporciöun.
Therwith the monës exaltaciöun,   10
I menë Libra, alwey gan ascende,
As we were entring at a thropës ende.
For which our Host, as he was wont to gye,
As in this caas, our joly companye,
Seide in this wisë : " Lordings everichoon,   15
Now lakketh us no talës mo than oon
(Fulfild is my sentence and my decree ;
I trowe that we han herd of ech degree) ;
Almost fulfi'd is al min ordinaunce ;
I prey to God : so yeve him right good chaunce   20
That telleth this tale to us lustily !

2-12 See Appendix 3 (iii).

7 *as there* ' there, where we
were, and at that hour, my
(Chaucer's) shadow was to my
height as 11 feet to 6 feet.'

10 See Appendix 3 (iv).

12 *thropes* thorp's, hamlet's.

13 *gye* ' guide, direct, in this
matter.'
17 *sentence* decision.
18 *of* ' tales from those of
every rank and position.'
21 *this tale* the one he is
about to call for : *lustily*
pleasantly, joyously.

I

Sir Preest," quod he, " art thou a vicary?
Or art a person ? Sey sooth, by thy fey!
Be what thou be, ne breke thou not our pley ;
For every man save thou hath told his tale.
Unbokel, and shew us what is in thy male ; 25
For trewëly me thinketh, by thy chere,
Thou sholdest knitte up wel a greet matere.
Tell us a fable anon, for cokkës bones ! "

Thís Persóun answérdë al at ones : 30
" Thou getest fable noon ytold for me ;
For Paul, that writeth unto Timothee,
Repreveth hem that weiven soothfastnesse,
And tellen fables and such wrecchednesse.
Why sholde I sowen draf out of my fest, 35
Whan I may sowen whete, if that me lest ?
For which I seye, if that you list to here
Moralitee and vertuous matere,
And than that ye wol yeve me audience,
I wol ful fain, at Cristes reverence, 40
Do you plesauncë leefful, as I can.
But trusteth wel, I am a southren man,
I can not gestë, ' rum, ram, ruf,' by lettre ;
Ne, God woot, rym holde I but lytel bettre ;
And therfore, if you list, I wol not glose, 45

22–3 *vicary* vicar : *person* rector.

24 *Be* ' whichever thou art.'

26 *Unbokel* unbuckle, open.

30 *al* ' at once.'

31 *fable* fictitious story : *for me* for my part.

32 *Timothee.* There are three passages, all referring to " fables " : 1 Tim. i. 4 and iv. 7, 2 Tim. iv. 4.

33 *weiven* waive, forsake.

35 *draf* chaff : *fest* fist.

36 *if* ' if it pleases me.'

39 *audience* hearing, attention.

40 *at* ' in honour of Christ.'

41 *Do* ' give you permissible pleasure.'

42 *southren* southern ; the well-known alliterative poems are not in the southern dialect.

43 ' I know not how to tell stories in alliterative metres, like the Northern and West Midland poets.' That no scorn of the alliterative poems is intended is clear from the next line.

44 *rym* rhyme.

45 *I wol not glose* without explanation or commentary.

I wol you telle a mery tale in prose,
To knitte up al this feste and make an ende.
And Jesu, for his gracë, wit me sende
To shewë you the wey, in this viáge,
Of thilkë parfit, glorious pilgrimage,   50
That highte Jerusalem celestiäl.
And if ye vouchësauf, anon I shal
Biginne upon my tale ; for which I preye,
Telle your avis : I can no bettre seye.
But natheles this meditaciöun   55
I putte it ay under correcciöun
Of clerkës, for I am not textuel ;
I takë but the sentence, trusteth wel ;
Therfore I makë protestaciöun
That I wol stondë to correcciöun."   60

Upon this word we han assented sone,
For, as us semëd, it was for to done,
To enden in som vertuous senténce,
And for to yeve him space and audiénce ;
And bad our Host he sholdë to him seye,   65
That allë we to telle his tale him preye.

Our Hostë hadde the wordës for us alle :
" Sir Preest," quod he, " now fairë you bifalle !
Sey what you list, and we wol gladly here."
And, with that word, he seide in this manere :   70
" Telleth," quod he, " your meditaciöun ;
But hasteth you, the sonnë wol adoun.
Beth fructuous, and that in lytel space ;
And to do wel God sendë you his grace ! "

(Here is the Parson's Tale in prose.)

---

47 *To knitte* ' to round off this festal holiday.'

49 *viage* journey.

50 *pilgrimage* end of our pilgrimage.

53 *which* sc. reason.

54 *avis* opinion, counsel.

57 *textuel* well acquainted with the authorities.

58 *trusteth wel* believe me.

62 *it was* ' it was the right thing to do.'

64 *space* opportunity.

65 *bede* we bade.

68 *now* ' now fair befall you ! '

73 *fructuous* fruitful.

APPENDIX

THE ZODIAC

[I have had great help with the Zodiac from two friends. Mr. C. W. C. Barlow, M.A., solved all difficulties presented to him, with the patience and skill of a born teacher. The following notes are, apart from slight alterations and the addition of (v) on p. 105, by Miss Algar of Exeter. I have only to add that readers attracted to the subject may like to purchase *The Revolving Star Map, with Movable Declination Scale*, by Mrs. H. P. Hawkins (Simpkin, Marshall & Co. 1s.).]

1. *Note on the Zodiac.*

The heavens were studied in detail in very early times, and the positions of the fixed stars were mapped by a system of measurement by angular distance. This system is more familiar to most people, under another aspect, than they suppose ; for it was applied by geographers to their maps of the earth, when the latter was explored and mapped as a sphere ; and our atlases are constructed on the same principle as the charts of the heavens. The correspondence is real ; the north and south poles of the earth lie vertically beneath the north and south poles of the sky, being in the same great axis ; the equator marks that line on the earth's surface which is exactly beneath the celestial equator ; and our meridians of longitude and parallels of latitude correspond respectively to the circles of right ascension passing through the celestial poles, and the circles of equal declination parallel to the celestial equator. The equatorial belt of the earth's surface, marked off by the Tropics of Cancer and Capricorn, is that part of the earth which lies vertically beneath the great

H

equatorial belt of the sky, limited by the celestial Tropics of
Cancer and Capricorn, where the sun actually appears to turn
southwards in summer and northwards in winter.

The *apparent* path of the sun in his annual circuit of the
heavens is called the ecliptic. It intersects the celestial

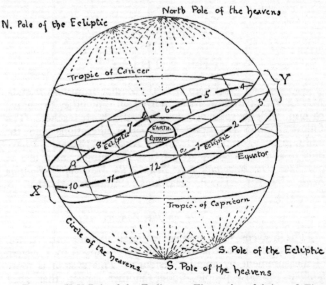

FIG. 1.—X Y Belt of the Zodiac. *a* First point of Aries ; *b* First
point of Libra. Oblong sections : 1. Aries, 2. Taurus, 3. Gemini,
4. Cancer, 5. Leo, 6. Virgo, 7. Libra, 8. Scorpio, 9 Sagittarius,
10. Capricorn, 11. Aquarius, 12. Pisces. The circles of right
ascension passing through the N. and S. Poles of the heavens, and
the circles of longitude passing through the poles of the ecliptic, are
slightly indicated ; but the circles of equal declination parallel to the
equator, and those of latitude parallel to the ecliptic, are entirely
omitted to avoid overcrowding the figure.

equator in two opposite points at an angle of 23½ degrees, so
that half of it is north and half south of that equator. Thus
it lies obliquely between the Tropic of Cancer, 23½ degrees
north, and that of Capricorn, 23½ degrees south, of the
equator.

The sun apparently traverses the whole circle (360 degrees) of the ecliptic in a year, travelling at an average rate of about a degree a day. At the vernal equinox, about March 21st, he crosses the equator at the " First Point of Aries," travelling northwards. About ninety-two days later, at Midsummer, he reaches the Tropic of Cancer, and turns southwards, crossing the equator again at the " First Point of Libra," at the autumn equinox. About Christmas he turns northward again on reaching the Tropic of Capricorn, and completes the year's journey at the equator about March 21st.

Since the moon and planets are always to be found near the ecliptic, the latter is the basis of another series of angular measurements. It has its own north and south poles, midway between which it lies, with circles of longitude passing through them, and circles of latitude parallel to the ecliptic itself. Thus celestial longitude and latitude have reference to the ecliptic ; they are employed to define the positions of the sun, moon, and planets with regard to it, and not to the equator.

The belt of twelve constellations through which the ecliptic passes is called the Zodiac. The name is ultimately derived from the Greek " Zoon," a living creature, because these constellations, or " Signs of the Zodiac," are chiefly represented as animal forms. This region of the sky has from very ancient times been thus specially distinguished from the rest, because the sun, moon, and planets are always to be found within its limits of 6 or 8 degrees on each side of the ecliptic. It is easily seen in the heavens by tracing among the stars the constellations of which it consists. But these constellations are of irregular extent, and for this reason the ancient astronomers, who were also astrologers, divided the Zodiac into twelve *equal* sections of 30 degrees each, measured along the 360 degrees of the ecliptic, beginning at the First Point of Aries. These sections of the Zodiac are still called by the names of the original signs, although, owing to the precession of the equinoxes, they now only partly coincide with the constellations whose names they bear, and this displacement constantly increases.

We are here concerned with these mathematical divisions of the Zodiac ; they, and not the original constellations, are the " signs " employed by the older astronomers, and by astrologers down to the present day, in defining the positions of the " planets." Under the latter term the sun and moon are included, since they, like the true planets, move among the fixed stars.

The names of the Signs are given in order in the old rhyme :

> The Ram, the Bull, the Heavenly Twins,
> And next the Crab, the Lion shines,
> The Virgin and the Scales ;
> The Scorpion, Archer, and He-goat,
> The Man that pours the water out,
> And Fish with glittering scales.

Otherwise : Aries, Taurus, Gemini, Cancer, Leo, Virgo ; Libra, Scorpio, Sagittarius, Capricornus, Aquarius, Pisces. The first six are northern signs, the last six southern.

Modern astronomy refers to the Zodiac only in the names given to the points in which the ecliptic intersects the equator, namely, the First Point of Aries and the First Point of Libra.

The connection of the Zodiac with the year is thus easily understood. The sun enters the " sign " Aries about March 21st, and passes through all the signs at the rate of about a degree a day, thus spending on an average a little more than thirty days in each throughout the year.

Hence Chaucer indicates dates by giving the position of the sun in the Zodiac. But in his day the accepted date was about nine days behind the real " world-time," so that the day of the vernal equinox, when the sun entered Aries, was then about March 12th. This date must, therefore, be taken as the starting-point of Chaucer's zodiacal reckoning.

2. *How Chaucer knew what constellations were behind the sun, when they were invisible in the daytime.*

Any special star or group of stars rises each night about four minutes earlier than it did the night before, so that in two or three weeks there is a noticeable difference in the face of the sky, and during a year all the stars visible in any given latitude become in turn well placed for observation. Thus they may easily be studied, and the principal groups learnt by reference to a map. Charts of the heavens were made in very ancient times, and the strange figures then assigned

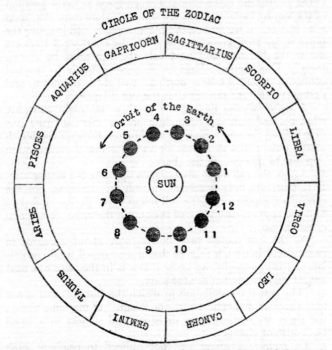

FIG. 2.—Diagram to show how the *actual* motion of the earth round the sun produces the *apparent* motion of the sun round the Zodiac. When the earth is passing through section 1 of the twelve sections of her course, the sun *appears* to observers on the earth to be passing through Aries ; as the earth " enters " the Scorpio section, the sun appears to " enter " Taurus, and so on. In short, when the earth is between the sun and any one sign, the sun appears against the opposite one as a *background*. It is the earth which really passes all the signs in her course : they all successively form a background for the stationary sun.

(A somewhat similar diagram explains the " retrograde " motions of the Planets.)

to the various groupings of the stars were, and are, a great help to memory.

Any one who can recognise the twelve great constellations of the Zodiac can make at least a rough guess as to the position of the sun by looking at the sky when the stars come out, soon after sunset ; if we find on the chart the stars visible above the horizon, we shall know at once from the chart what stars are below the horizon, and obviously the sun must be among these. This method, however, is most suitable to tropical countries, where the long northern twilight is unknown, and darkness falls very rapidly after the sun disappears.

A better way is to face the south at midnight and note what constellation is culminating on the meridian (the line drawn from the south point of the horizon through the zenith to the pole) ; the sun must be in the zodiacal constellation opposite to that one on the chart.

Again, the *full* moon always rises opposite the setting sun. It is therefore only necessary to wait for darkness, observe carefully the position of the full moon in the Zodiac, and then find the approximate place of the sun in the opposite zodiacal constellation.

As the sun moves very slowly (only about a degree in twenty-four hours), it follows that if we can tell what constellation it is in at night, we know that it is in the same one next day, though we do not see the stars.

(The actual constellation in which the sun is found is not now necessarily identical with the " sign " of the same name ; the signs are mathematical divisions and subject to a small but constant change.)

Of course, Chaucer was not obliged to use any such empirical method. The angular measurements now in use were invented by the ancients, and Chaucer was himself the writer of a treatise on the Astrolabe, an instrument used in an early form by the Chaldæan and Greek astronomers, and employed as late as the end of the sixteenth century by the great Danish astronomer, Tycho Brahé. Before the Christian era, great progress was made in mapping the heavens and systematically recording the movements, both real and apparent, of stars, sun, moon, and planets. Later, the Arab astronomers greatly advanced the science. Thus in Chaucer's time it was as inevitable for an astronomer to be able to refer the sun to its correct degree in the proper sign of the Zodiac on any given day as it is now for a ship's navigator to do

precisely the same thing in other terms by looking up the
date and the sun's longitude in the Nautical Almanac. Each
statement expresses after its own fashion the distance of the
sun from the First Point of Aries.

3. Special Passages.

(i) A.7, 8 (not in this volume):

> " The yongë sonne
> Hath in the Ram his halfë cours yronne."

As we are told that the month is April, this necessarily refers
to the second half of Aries, as Skeat has pointed out. The
sun enters the Ram on March 12th; the first half of the sign
is completely traversed on March 27th, fifteen days later;
and the second half is completed in another fifteen days, on
April 11th.

The sun actually takes about 30 days 11½ hours to go
through Aries; thus, if he happen to enter the sign late in the
day, it is not until the thirty-first day after that he leaves it.
But it is clear that Chaucer reckons only the average thirty days.

(ii) B.4383–5 (not in this volume):

> " The brightë sonne
> That in the signe of Taurus had yronne
> Twenty degrees and oon and somewhat more."

Entering Taurus on April 11th, the sun would have passed
through 21 degrees some time on May 2nd. The "somewhat more" brings us to the early part of May 3rd, and
Chaucer indicates the time of day by saying that the sun had
reached an altitude of 41 degrees (l. 4389). He has been calculated to attain that altitude about 9 a.m. at that time of year.
Thus early in the day the sun had not completely traversed
the twenty-second degree of Taurus; later he would have
done so. (The length of a degree on the ecliptic is about
twice the apparent diameter of the sun, so that he travels
through that space of the heavens, on an average, each day.)

(iii) I.2–12:

> " The sonnë fro the south line was descended
> So lowë that he nas not, to my sighte,
> Degreës nine and twenty as in highte.

> Four of the clokke it was tho, as I gesse ;
> For eleven foot, or lytel more or lesse,
> My shadwe was at thilkë time, as there,
> Of such feet as my lengthë parted were
> In six feet equal of proporciöun.
> Therwith the monës exaltaciöun,
> I menë Libra, alwey gan ascende,
> As we were entring. . . ."

The " south line " is the meridian passing through the pole, the zenith, and the south point of the horizon ; at mean noon the sun is on or near it. To indicate the time of day, Chaucer gives the altitude of the sun as 29 degrees, no doubt ascertaining it by inspection of an astrolabe, an old instrument, now superseded, for observing altitude by inspection. He enlarges on the idea by giving also the proportion of his height to his shadow ; the angle whose tangent is $\frac{6}{11}$ is practically 29 degrees.

The MSS. give " ten " o'clock instead of " four " ; but as 10 p.m. would be after sunset, change is necessary. The altitude of the sun being 29 degrees, and the day of the year about April 20th, the actual time of day must have been about 4 p.m. Mr. Brae suggests that the reading " ten " may have been a gloss on " four," since 4 o'clock is the tenth hour of the day, reckoning from 6 a.m. The fifth degree of Libra would be rising about 4 o'clock on April 20th.

(iv) I.10 :

" The monës exaltaciöun."

In astrology, each sign of the Zodiac is allotted to a special planet as its " house," the term " planet " including the sun and moon. Some planets have two houses. When in its own house, a planet is supposed to exercise its maximum influence on mundane affairs. The sign in which it exerts a less, but still important, influence is called its " exaltation," and certain degrees in other signs where its power is but slight are called its " terms " and, least powerful of all, its " face." Thus Cancer is the moon's own sign ; in Taurus she has her " exaltation," while her " face " is the first ten degrees of Libra. But Libra is the " exaltation " of Saturn, and, as

Chaucer must have known this quite well, it is hardly to be supposed that he made a slip. He may have purposely called Libra the " exaltacioun " of the moon because of the rhyme with " proporcioun " in the previous line. A planet is said to be " dignified " in a sign where it has any special influence, so that there is a very small justification astrologically.

Tyrwhitt suggests that " the mones " is an error for " Saturnes." In support of this most probable explanation may be adduced an article in the *Athenæum* of May, 1902, by R. Garnett, in which he wrote : " It is impossible that Chaucer should have been in error on such a subject. The difficulty probably arises from ' Saturn ' having been expressed in the archetypal MS. by its astronomical symbol, which was mistaken for the symbol of the moon. Both are curved in shape, the one denoting the lunar crescent, the other the crooked pruning-knife emblematic of Saturn. The handle of the latter is represented by a perpendicular stroke. If this were omitted, or indistinctly delineated, the symbols might easily be confused."

This explanation of the error is not only ingenious, but extremely probable ; such an error might very well take place in copying.

(v) B.1–14 :

> Our Hostë saw wel that the brightë sonne
> The ark of his artificial day hath ronne
> The fourthë part, and half an hour and more ;
> And, though he were not depe expert in lore,
> He wist it was the eightëtethë day
> Of April that is messager to May ;
> And saw wel that the shadwe of every tree
> Was, as in length, the samë quantitee
> That was the body erect that causëd it ;
> And therfore by the shadwe he took his wit
> That Phebus, which that shoon so clere and brighte,
> Degrees was five and fourty clombe on highte ;
> And for that day, as in that latitude,
> It was ten of the clokke, he gan conclude.

This passage does not involve the Zodiac, but this seems the best place to deal with it.

The " artificial day " is from sunrise to sunset, as distinguished from the natural day of 24 hours. The fourth part of the artificial day at that time of year would have elapsed at about half-past eight. But the Host's " fourth part " was the time taken by the sun in traversing a quarter of the distance between the point of sunrise and the point of sunset *on the horizon ;* his *arc* was the part of the horizon-circle between the points of sunrise and sunset. Now it is obvious that the sun takes much longer to traverse the first and last fourths of this distance than is occupied in traversing the two middle fourths. (If this is not obvious, let the reader place a door in a narrow passage half open, and see how much farther the edge of the door is from one wall than the other ; that is to say, if the door is opened wide at an even speed, in half the time it will not have covered nearly half the distance between the two walls.) Mr. A. E. Brae, who first explained this passage, calculated that a fourth part of the horizontal distance between the points of sunrise and sunset would have been traversed, at this time of the year, at *twenty minutes past nine*. Add to this " half an hour and more " (l. 3), and we get " ten of the clokke " (l. 14).

But the Host also observed that the shadow of every tree was equal in length to the tree's height, and concluded that the sun's altitude was 45 degrees (ll. 7–12). Geometrically, the tree and its shadow made a right angle, or 90 degrees ; if the line of the shadow were extended to the sun's side of the tree, that would also make a right angle, which the rays of the sun bisected, again giving 45 degrees. Mr. Brae calculated that on April 18th then (=April 27th now) the sun attained an altitude of 45 degrees exactly at *two minutes to ten*. Hence the date and the hour are both confirmed.

INDEX

The following words are explained in the notes on the lines whose numbers follow them :

abide, A3129
acquit, B37
after, D346
again, C427
age, D174
aken, B2113
al, B2138
al and som, D91
algate, C292, D588
alle and some, A3136
also (=as), D825
and (=if), E2433
anoye, B3979
apaid, B1897
apeiren, A3147
aright, A3115
array, D289
artow, D240
as, B8, E7
assay, D286
assoille, C387
at erst, B1884
atte, B38
Austin, B1631
avalen, A3122
aventure, C934
aviseth you, A3185
avisement, B86
axen, D21, E25
ay, E2422

benedicite, B1170
bere on hond, D380
bet, D775
beth, B1629
bishrewe, D844

biwreye, D533
blering, A3865
brawn, B3131
brenne, D374
but (=unless), D360
but-if, A3156
by, D229
bye, D167

can, B1169
care, H54
catel, B27
certes, B1898
chaunce, F679
chere, B97
cherl, A3169
chese, A3177
cheste, D502
clappe, B3971
clepe, B61, 3169
clerk, C339
clombe, B12
cofre, B26
cokewold, C382
conseil, D82
contrarius, D698
cope, B3139
corny, C315
corpus bones, B3096
cors, C304
coveitise, A3884

dan, daun, B3119
daungerous, B2129
deed, E29
defend, D60

107

THE END

PRINTED IN GREAT BRITAIN BY
WILLIAM CLOWES AND SONS, LIMITED,
LONDON AND BECCLES.